THE BIRDS OF ORANGE COUNTY, CALIFORNIA
STATUS AND DISTRIBUTION

Figure 1 - Cactus Wren in Prickly-Pear   Sandra Harvill

THE
BIRDS OF ORANGE COUNTY
CALIFORNIA
STATUS AND DISTRIBUTION

By

ROBERT A. HAMILTON

and

DOUGLAS R. WILLICK

SEA & SAGE PRESS

SEA & SAGE AUDUBON SOCIETY

IRVINE, CALIFORNIA

ISBN 0-9650311-0-1

Library of Congress Catalog Card Number: 96-69070

Published by: Sea & Sage Press
                 Sea & Sage Audubon Society
                 P.O. Box 5447
                 Irvine, California 92616-5447

This book uses soy-based inks on acid-free, recycled paper bleached without the use of chlorine. Printed in the United States by Wholesale Press, Fountain Valley, California.

Design and typesetting by Allan J. Der and Robert A. Hamilton.

Cover: Clapper Rail with Fiddler Crab, original scratchboard by John Schmitt; computer design by Allan J. Der.

Back Cover: California Gnatcatcher, original pen-and-ink by Sandra Harvill.

Illustrations by Sandra Harvill, John Schmitt and Kris Walden.

Maps by Kris Walden and Robert A. Hamilton

Suggested citation:

Hamilton, R.A., and D.R. Willick. 1996. The Birds of Orange County, California: Status and Distribution. Sea & Sage Press, Sea & Sage Audubon Society, Irvine.

Dedicated to our parents

and to every person
who values places
over things

Figure 1 - Northern Harrier Food Exchange

John Schmitt

Contents

Figures

Appendices

Foreword

Orange County is the smallest of the southern California counties. The coast and adjacent lowlands are highly developed, the mountains are low in comparison to those in adjacent counties, and there is no desert. As such, the area would appear unlikely to support an impressive variety of bird species.

However, marshlands and other coastal habitats have been preserved along the shore, urban parks supporting a variety of plantings are scattered throughout the lowlands, and large areas of native habitat remain in the foothills and mountains, this all favoring a large assortment of bird species. Add to this a group of knowledgeable birders actively competing in friendly listing games year after year, and the variety of species recorded in this county has increased to a truly impressive number.

This book not only provides accurate information on the status and seasonal abundance of bird species occurring in Orange County, but also specifies their preferred habitats and the best locations to search for each. This will make it a useful tool for visiting birders seeking local specialties. With respect to seasonal abundance and habitat requirements, the information is relevant to the region as a whole. It is a book that every southern California birder should own.

Guy McCaskie

Acknowledgments

Willis E. Pequegnat undertook the first effort to document and describe the occurrence of birds in a major portion of Orange County as part of pioneering biological studies that he conducted in the Santa Ana Mountains between 1937 and 1951. His 1951 publication, The Biota of the Santa Ana Mountains, provides important historical information on the plants, herpetiles, birds and mammals of our local mountains, and is peppered with colorful tales of mountain life. It belongs in the libraries of more southern California naturalists. Charles W. Sexton and George L. Hunt, Jr. first described the status and distribution of bird life county-wide with An Annotated Checklist of the Birds of Orange County, California, edited by Gordon A. Marsh and published by the University of California (UC) Irvine Museum of Systematic Biology in 1979. The original manuscript was completed in 1974, and the finished book covered only selected subsequent records through 1977. Sexton and Hunt conducted extensive historical research, and their treatment of former status is more detailed than ours for many species. We encourage readers to obtain this out-of-print book while it is still available through the UC Irvine Department of Biological Sciences. In seeking to recognize the many people who have contributed to our present knowledge of Orange County birds, we start with Pequegnat, Sexton and Hunt.

The seeds of this project were sown during the depths of the Reagan era as Robb Hamilton's senior research project at UC Irvine. During this formative period, Jon L. Dunn, H. Lee Jones, Paul E. Lehman, and advisors Peter Bowler and George L. Hunt provided guidance, support and helpful reviews. For providing advice on and access to a dizzying procession of computers during this period and after, thanks to Louis R. Bevier, Charles F. and Margaret A. Hamilton, Richard Hartman, Dave Keller, Mark F. Mou, Beth and Chris Padon, Michael Brandman Associates and H. Hendy Associates.

The following people and institutions provided information on bird specimens, egg sets, band recoveries and field notes: Charles T. Collins at the California State University at Long Beach, Kimball L. Garrett at the Natural History Museum of Los Angeles County, Ned K. Johnson and Barbara R. Stein at the UC Berkeley Museum of Vertebrate Zoology, Robert L. McKernan at the San Bernardino Museum of Natural History, Philip Unitt at the San Diego Natural History Museum, Jon C. Fisher and Walter Wehtje at the Western Foundation of Vertebrate Zoology, and W.J. Hillenius at the Dickey Collection, UC Los Angeles. The birding community too seldom acknowledges our debt to these talented people and their predecessors, who collected, prepared, cataloged and preserved tens of thousands of specimens for our edification. We encourage readers to acquaint themselves with these collections and to invest in their continued existence.

For their contributions of notes and suggestions, we are pleased to recognize Charles Hood, Gordon L. Marsh and Brad K. Schram. Paul F. Springer's authoritative assistance and detective work solidified our treatment of Canada Geese. Ted Swem of U.S. Fish and Wildlife Service Ecological Services in Fairbanks, Alaska, provided information on Tundra Peregrine Falcons that he banded on the Coleville River, and a healthy dose of circumspection regarding field identification of Peregrine Falcon subspecies. Janet Linthicum of the Santa Cruz Predatory Bird Research Group relayed information on recent American Peregrine Falcon nesting activities in Orange County and on a Tundra Peregrine Falcon sighting. Richard R. Veit provided data collected offshore during CALCOFI research cruises (cf. Cheltan et al. 1982). Howard L. Cogswell provided a summary of Bald Eagle records. Kurt F. Campbell assisted with last-minute research of selected species.

Sea & Sage Audubon Society contributed to this project in many important ways. First, kudos to Trude E. Hurd and volunteers at Sea & Sage Audubon House for maintaining and summarizing records of bird sightings at San Joaquin Marsh. Sea & Sage board member Sylvia L. Gallagher graciously provided an early draft of the Orange County Breeding Bird Atlas, improving our treatment of many nesting species. Many thanks to Ms. Gallagher and all of the Breeding Bird Atlas volunteers for helping to elucidate the breeding status of Orange County birds. We were happy and fortunate to have Sea & Sage member Sabrina Nicholls proofread a late draft of this book. We appreciate the time and effort that Sea & Sage Audubon Society board members Sam A. Berry, Christopher J. Obaditch and Susan H. Sheakley put into this project, and particularly thank Sea & Sage member Allan J. Der for the many hours he spent preparing the book for press.

LSA Associates and P&D Consultants provided supplies and other support during the project's twilight years. LSA graphics wizard and neo-cartographer Kris Walden produced final maps based on drafts prepared by Hamilton. N. John Schmitt, Sandra G. Harvill and Kris Walden contributed striking original artwork. Denis and Jane Clarke of Source Books and W. David Shuford of the Point Reyes Bird Observatory generously provided a range of helpful suggestions regarding printing and publishing.

The following people reviewed the final draft manuscript, or portions of it, for content: Peter H. Bloom (raptors), Jeffrey S. Boyd, Charles T. Collins (terns), Brian E. Daniels, Sylvia L. Gallagher, Kimball L. Garrett, Wayne R. Gochenour, Loren R. Hays, Matthew T. Heindel, Michael A. Patten, James E. Pike, Charles W. Sexton, Gerald L. Tolman and Richard R. Veit (seabirds).

We greatly appreciate their time and effort, and know that this book benefitted significantly from their many incisive suggestions.

Richard A. Erickson came closer to serving as editor than any other person. His particularly thorough reviews and many good advices raised the quality and usefulness of this book to a level beyond our expectations. Special thanks to a great friend and mentor.

Finally, we thank our families and all of our friends for their patience and support.

Figure 3 - Adult Least Tern with Chick   Kris Walden

Introduction

This guide indicates when, where, and in what relative quantity birds are encountered in Orange County. Bar graphs depict week-to-week abundance and breeding status of 441 native species recorded in the county as of 29 February 1996. Recognizable subspecies and races are treated to the extent they are known. Annotations amplify data presented in the bar graphs. Hypothetical records and non-native species are treated after the main text. The checklist in Appendix A includes common and scientific names for all species and field-identifiable subspecies recorded. Maps in Appendix B show 1) the area considered in this book, 2) Orange County birding locations, and 3) topography and major features.

Area Considered

This book covers the politically established terrestrial boundaries of Orange County, plus a triangular offshore area that extends from the Los Angeles County line to the southeast tip of Santa Catalina Island (excluding any part of the island), then due east to the San Diego County line (Map 1, Appendix B). In establishing this offshore area, we canvassed many active southern California birders and found that "customary" pelagic boundaries (i.e., limits recognized by most local birders) do not really exist for Orange County. The area that we treat does not cross significantly into waters regularly covered by San Diego or Los Angeles county birders, is simple to chart at sea, and encourages exploration of local pelagic waters.

The California Bird Records Committee is a select panel of birders that 1) evaluates all vagrant records of statewide significance, and 2) maintains the "official" state list, a task involving analysis of all species, vagrant or not, native or exotic. Patten et al. (1995) provided an overview of the Committee's history, purpose, and interactions with the birding community; Heindel and Patten (1996) reported the Committee's latest decisions at the time of publication. For the Committee's purposes, oceanic waters assume the political identity of the nearest piece of land. Under these guidelines, Los Angeles County takes in Santa Catalina and San Clemente islands and surrounding waters, leaving Orange County a roughly rectangular offshore area that extends approximately 13 miles from the coast. For the purposes of evaluating and cataloging vagrant records of statewide significance, these boundaries define offshore Orange County. No records of Committee-reviewed species have occurred between this line and the southeast tip of Santa Catalina Island.

How *(and Why)* to Use This Book

We have structured this book to provide a great volume of detailed information clearly and concisely, so that readers may quickly gain a working knowledge of bird status and distribution in Orange County. The book's main body describes the status of all native species and field-identifiable subspecies whose occurrence in Orange County has been demonstrated to our satisfaction. Less clear-cut records are treated in a Supplemental List, and introduced and exotic species are discussed in a section at the back. Bar graphs depict the relative abundance of each native species recorded in the county from week to week, with particularly unusual records shown individually. Annotations complement the graphs, providing dates of individual records, historic status, and other textual information. This book also recommends locations for finding birds in Orange County, and provides descriptions of the county's physical environment and major habitats.

The first step in using this book is to become familiar with the bar graph format by examining the key on page 34. Although perhaps intimidating at first glance, the graphs are intuitive and simple to read with a little practice. For each species treated in the main body of the text, one or more graphs provide the following information where applicable:

Habitat Code: A simple code identifies the generalized habitat type(s) where a given species regularly occurs, or where unusual species could be reasonably expected. Abundance is not necessarily constant among listed habitats; multiple graphs are often employed where the status varies significantly between habitats.

Abundance: The graphed abundance reflects the authors' best estimate of each species' week-to-week status; in many cases, annotations clarify the graphed status. Particularly unusual records are graphed individually and annotated.

Breeding Status: The current/historic breeding status is shown in the second column from the right. We identify some species as breeders based on strong circumstantial evidence and our best judgment, rather than direct observation of nesting; this is discussed in the annotations.

Site Guide: Found in the rightmost column, this bird-finding feature provides recommendations for viewing a given species in the county, considering factors such as seasonal consistency and site accessibility. In general, sites are not recommended for species that are not regularly found at a single locale. All recommended sites are shown on Map 2 in Appendix B.

Methods

This book covers records through 29 February 1996; end-dates extend into April 1996 for a few records of overwintering vagrants.

Classification and nomenclature follow the sixth edition of the American Ornithologists' Union Checklist (1983) through the 40th supplement (1996), except as otherwise noted. Due to space considerations, full scientific names are included only in the Appendix A checklist. We have considered field-identifiable subspecies and races to the extent they are known, but recognize that the possibility of error increases as observers attempt to identify birds to subspecific levels in the field. Moreover, research at the molecular level continually calls into question taxonomic assumptions based on outward appearances. Unless the annotations discuss supporting specimen evidence, readers should consider subspecific records as "birds showing characteristics of" the indicated taxon. For sterner warnings, see Monson and Phillips (1981 pp. xv-xxiii). Despite these limitations, we feel that readers and the scientific process will benefit from closer treatment of birds that show clear differences in morphology, plumage and/or voice.

Since 1979, Sylvia L. Gallagher and Willick have compiled and edited the Orange County seasonal reports to *American Birds* and *National Audubon Society Field Notes*. Copies of these reports have been archived at Sea & Sage Audubon House, located in Irvine (on Riparian View Road off Michelson Avenue, next to the Irvine Ranch Water District treatment plant). The phone number is (714) 261-7963, and the mailing address is P.O. Box 5447, Irvine, CA 92616-5447. Most individually annotated records in this book are taken from the seasonal reports, and many have been published in the above-mentioned magazines or their predecessor, *Audubon Field Notes*. Acceptable records from the seasonal reports and other acceptable records published in these magazines are published herein without citation. Observer initials are provided for 1) corrections to published and unpublished records, and 2) records not included in seasonal reports. We consider many older (pre-1979) records unacceptable due to lack of supporting documentation and/or lack of familiarity with observer skills. We are particularly skeptical of many older Christmas Bird Count records due to discovery of an uncomfortably large number of obvious errors interspersed among intriguing, but unsubstantiated, reports of rare species. Unacceptable records published in books or peer-reviewed journals are treated in the annotations. Unacceptable records published elsewhere (e.g., the above-mentioned magazines) are generally omitted without discussion.

As indicated previously, the California Bird Records Committee evaluates all vagrant records of statewide significance. In order for the Committee to sanction a given record, at least nine of the ten Committee members must vote to accept the record within four rounds of review. Committee decisions are published regularly in *Western Birds* (Vol. 27:1-29 contains the latest report at time of publication). No accepted records have been omitted from this book and no rejected records are published here, although some merit mention in the Supplemental List. Sightings that we consider reliable and that are under Committee review at the time of publication, or that certainly will be submitted for review in the near future, are marked (*) in the annotations. Sightings of species on the Committee's review list that we consider reliable, but which are unlikely to ever be submitted for Committee review, are marked (ø) in the annotations.

Unless otherwise noted, statements regarding average numbers of seasonal sightings represent post-1980 data. This primarily reflects our understanding that local birder activity, skill levels, and thoroughness of documentation each began to rise steadily around that time. For example, only two fall migrant Northern Waterthrushes were found in Orange County between 1963 and 1979, a pattern inconsistent with Garrett and Dunn's (1981) characterization of this species as a rare, regular fall migrant in coastal southern California. From 1980 to 1995, however, a new focus on searching out scarce migrants resulted in detection of at least 35 fall migrant Northern Waterthrushes in the county. While we believe that the dramatic increase in records of rare species has primarily resulted from changes in observer coverage, convincing evidence shows that many "southern" and "eastern" species are, in fact, occurring more frequently in the West (DeSante 1983, Terrill et al. 1992, Johnson 1994, Pyle et al. 1994, Patten and Marantz 1996). Again using Northern Waterthrush as an example, detection of seven spring migrants in Orange County between 1989 and 1995 suggests that this species may be occurring more frequently during this season, since Garrett and Dunn (1981) reported only "a few spring records" for all of coastal southern California.

Abundance and seasonal movements specified in the bar graphs and annotations reflect our understanding of each species' overall pattern of occurrence in Orange County as determined through 1) review of field notes, 2) review of records submitted to the magazines *Audubon Field Notes*, *American Birds* and *National Audubon Society Field Notes*, and 3) review of literature describing the local and regional avifauna. Summaries of daily logs maintained by Sea & Sage Audubon Society volunteers at San Joaquin Marsh since fall 1992 provided valuable data regarding the status of waterfowl and shorebirds at this important wetland area. Inevitably, the graphs also incorporate the "impressions" of the authors and other local and regional authorities. For numeric consistency, the graphs are best interpreted by comparing related species (e.g., hawks with other hawks). Recognizing that the "uncommon to fairly common" bar covers a rather wide range of occurrence, we have clarified this designation to the best of our abilities in the annotations.

The bar graphs simplify often complex movement patterns, some of which remain indistinct even after years of observations and record keeping. We have remained as true to the Orange County records as possible in assembling the graphs, and acknowledge the increased risk of error associated with extrapolating species' local status from data gathered elsewhere. Unfortunately, birder coverage of the far offshore waters and the Santa Ana Mountains remains inadequate to determine the status of several species based strictly on county records. In cases where the graphed status is based primarily on data from outside the county, this is specified in the annotations.

Readers should also bear in mind that numbers of migrants passing through a given area typically vary somewhat from year to year due to fluctuating populations and vagaries in weather patterns; for scarce migrants, this variability is further magnified by the "hit and miss" nature of birding. For example, small numbers of Gray Flycatchers undoubtedly filter through local riparian areas, parks and gardens each year during the latter half of April (graphed as "rare and regular"), with less predictable numbers occurring in early April and early May (graphed as "casual to rare and irregular"). While two or three Gray Flycatchers are typically detected in spring, this number has ranged from zero in 1981, 1986 and 1988, to an astonishing total of 20 in 1995. Since relatively few "rare, regular" migrants have been detected every single year since 1980, these species should be considered "virtually regular."

We have specified the age and/or sex of unusual records when this information is known and considered reliable. Additional age/sex information for specific records may be found in the seasonal reports on file at Audubon House. The occurrence of age classes is discussed where such information 1) is known, 2) is particularly relevant, and 3) may be summarized briefly.

Topography and Major Features

Situated between the Pacific Ocean and the spine of the Santa Ana Mountains, Orange County covers 782 square miles, the smallest land mass of any county in southern California. Nonetheless, Orange County boasts offshore waters, rocky shorelines, sandy beaches, coastal estuaries, large urban parks, exotic plantings, mesas, foothills and mountains, a diversity of habitats attractive to a wide variety of breeding, wintering and migrant birds. This section describes the gross underwater topography off the coast and provides the lay of the land. To interpret the information in this section, readers are encouraged to refer to the maps in Appendix B.

The nearshore underwater topography is dramatic from the San Diego County line to Corona del Mar, the sub-surface elevation falling off approximately 1500 feet within two to three miles of the coast. In contrast, the 100-foot contour lurks approximately three miles off Huntington Beach Pier and eight miles off Seal Beach Pier. Two submarine canyons, Newport and San Gabriel, lie just off the Balboa Peninsula and a few miles off Huntington Beach, respectively. The county's most attractive area for pelagic birding is Lausen Knoll and the associated 14 Mile Bank, which form a three-mile-long, south-west facing escarpment approximately 13 miles southwest of the mouth of Newport Harbor; elevations drop off sharply from 450 to 2100 feet along the length of this underwater cliff. Eight miles northeast of Avalon, Avalon Knoll and the associated 228 Fathom Bank form a north facing escarpment four miles long that ranges between 1350 and 2400 feet below sea level.

Map 3 in Appendix B depicts the major topographic features above sea-level. Dominant among these are the Santa Ana Mountains, which rise to a peak elevation of 5687 feet at Santiago Peak. The crest of this range, or "Main Divide," forms the county's eastern boundary, including the following named peaks (listed from north to south, elevations given in feet): Sierra (3045), Pleasant's (4007), Bedford (approximately 3800), Bald (3947), Modjeska (5496), Santiago (5687), Trabuco (4604) and Los Piños (4510). The north-ernmost mountain canyons, Coal and Gypsum, drain directly north into the Santa Ana River. Otherwise, the northern two-thirds of the coastal slope drains southwest into Santiago Creek. This major Santa Ana River tributary flows northwest across the base of the mountains, dumping into Irvine Lake (behind Santiago Dam) at its midpoint. From northwest to southeast, the major mountain canyons feeding Irvine Lake are Black Star, Baker, Ladd, Silverado, Williams, Harding and Modjeska.

Santiago Creek also drains the inland slope of Loma Ridge, an unassuming, largely undeveloped line of foothills reaching elevations of 1200-1800 feet. Loma Ridge parallels the Santa Anas between Cowan Heights to the north-west and Aliso Creek to the southeast, and contributes to Santiago Creek via Limestone Canyon. Below Irvine Lake, Santiago Creek bisects Irvine Regional Park, accepts flows from the mountains via Fremont, Blind and Weir canyons, then stacks up again in the flood control basin behind Villa Park Dam, which supports some of the county's most extensive willow woodlands. Northwest of here, the mostly developed Peralta Hills drain north and west toward the Santa Ana River via Walnut Canyon (Walnut Reservoir), and southward to Santiago Creek. Below Villa Park Dam, Santiago Creek flows northwest through the linear Santiago Oaks Regional Park, then bends southwest before ponding in large gravel pits. In this stretch, Handy Creek contributes flows from Peters Canyon Reservoir and Orange Park Acres. The parched lower section of Santiago Creek limps southwest through the cities of El Modena, Orange and Santa Ana, joining the Santa Ana River where Interstate 5 and State Route 22 converge.

San Juan Creek drains the southern third of the Santa Ana Mountains. From west to east, Trabuco (including Holy Jim and Falls canyons), Bell, Cold Springs and Hot Springs canyons are the major higher elevation tributaries to San Juan Creek. The upper portions of Trabuco and Bell canyons flow westerly, bending south as they enter the north/south trending foothill ridges of southern Orange County. From west to east, the major middle elevation tributaries to San Juan Creek are the Arroyo Trabuco (including flows from Rose, Hickey, Live Oak, Trabuco and Tijeras canyons), Cañada Chiquita, Cañada Gobernadora (including Wagon Wheel Canyon) and Bell Canyon (including Dove, Fox and Crow canyons). Plano Trabuco, an expansive shortgrass mesa wedged between the Arroyo Trabuco and Tijeras Creek at the base of the mountains, was turned into housing, commercial centers, business parks and warehouses in the late 1980s and early 1990s. No comparable area remains in Orange County.

Foothills directly west of the Arroyo Trabuco lie within the Aliso and Oso creek watersheds. Aliso Creek passes through Lake Forest, where it collects flows from English Canyon and continues toward the Pacific Ocean. Oso Creek passes through Oso Reservoir and Lake Mission Viejo, then runs straight south through Mission Viejo, flowing alongside Interstate 5 for approximately five miles before joining the Arroyo Trabuco in San Juan Capistrano. To the east, Horno Creek flows southwest into San Juan Creek near its confluence with the Arroyo Trabuco. Eastern tributaries to San Juan Creek from the Santa Margarita Mountains include Lucas, Verdugo and Trampas canyons.

In extreme southeast Orange County, Cristianitos Creek collects flows from Cristianitos, Gabino (including La Paz and Blind canyons) and Talega canyons, conveying these waters south to San Mateo Creek in San Diego County. The county line meets the Pacific Ocean at San Mateo Point, which marks the southeastern end of the Capistrano Bight. Approximately eight direct miles up the coast, just north of Dana Point Harbor and the mouth of San Juan Creek, Dana Point forms this bight's northwestern terminus. The coastal watersheds of Deep Canyon, Segunda Deschecha Cañada and Prima Deschecha Cañada, which flow into the Capistrano Bight, have been filled for roads and residential development along the coast, while San Juan Creek is lined with concrete below Interstate 5.

Between Dana Point and Laguna Niguel, Salt Creek (including remnants of Sulphur Creek and the Arroyo Salada along Crown Valley Parkway) carries runoff from the coastal hills to the Pacific Ocean. West of Laguna Niguel and northwest of South Laguna, Aliso and Wood canyons in the Sheep Hills flow south to the ocean via lower Aliso Creek. Continuing up the coast, Hobo and Bluebird canyons convey flows southwest toward the ocean through developed portions of Laguna Beach.

Northwest of Laguna Beach, the narrow coastal terrace lifts to form the beautiful San Joaquin Hills, which parallel the coast for approximately seven miles. These hills gradually build in elevation from south to north, reaching 1164 feet at Signal Peak. The coastal slope drains into the ocean via Laguna, Boat, Emerald, Moro, Muddy and Los Trancos canyons, and Buck Gully, located west of Pelican Hill (716 feet). Near Laguna Canyon's midpoint, between the San Joaquin Hills and the Sycamore Hills, lie the three Laguna Lakes, the only natural lakes in Orange County.

The inland slopes of the San Joaquin Hills lie within the vast San Diego Creek watershed. Shady and Bommer canyons flow north into Sand Canyon Reservoir. The outflow of this impoundment enters Sand Canyon Wash and flows northward into William R. Mason Regional Park, curls to the west around French Hill (426 feet), then passes through more than two miles of natural and created willow woodlands before merging with the San Diego Creek flood control channel just above San Joaquin Marsh, which is the county's largest extant freshwater marsh (approximately 850 acres). Bonita Creek (including the remnants of Coyote Canyon) flows northwest into the deep silt and dense willow woodlands of Bonita Reservoir. Below the dam, the creek continues through an extensive wetland mitigation area along the route of the San Joaquin Hills Transportation Corridor, entering San Diego Creek just above Upper Newport Bay.

San Diego Creek's remaining watershed includes numerous channelized washes that flow off the coastal slope of Loma Ridge and out of the north-eastern San Joaquin Hills (from Laguna and Veeh reservoirs). From east to west, the primary Loma Ridge tributaries are Serrano Creek, Borrego Canyon, Agua Chinon Wash (originating in a badlands formation called "The Sinks"), Round and Bee canyons (Lambert Reservoir), Hicks Canyon Wash (Siphon Reservoir), Rattlesnake Canyon Wash (Rattlesnake Reservoir) and Peters Canyon Wash (Peters Canyon Reservoir).

At the mouth of San Diego Creek lies Upper Newport Bay, the largest coastal estuary in southern California. Although rimmed by housing, the bay and surrounding bluffs retain high biological values for a variety of wildlife, including several threatened and endangered bird species. In the 1980s, dredge spoils and sand intentionally deposited near the bay's upper end formed two small islands that rapidly attracted nesting populations of terns, skimmers and other birds. Pacific Coast Highway divides Upper Newport Bay from Lower Newport Bay, a highly developed navigable waterway that once ushered flows from the Santa Ana River to the Pacific Ocean. The lower bay surrounds a few completely developed islands, the largest of which are Balboa and Lido.

Continuing northwest up the coast, we encounter the mouth of the Santa Ana River flood control channel, the county's primary watercourse. Although now locked in place between Newport Beach and Huntington Beach, the mighty river mouth historically wandered several miles between Anaheim Bay and Newport Bay, feeding the vast Gospel Swamp (described subsequently under Avian Population Trends). The channelized lower river, south of Anaheim, flows through miles of intensely developed floodplain and coastal terrace, mostly between 50 and 300 feet elevation. Although most of the natural communities bordering the lower river have been degraded or destroyed, remnant wetlands and uplands in Costa Mesa and Newport Beach retain important biological values.

Approaching the Los Angeles County line, we pass the expansive, hydrologically linked Bolsa Chica Ecological Preserve, Sunset Aquatic Park, and Anaheim Bay, once part of the Santa Ana River ecosystem. Anaheim Bay, the county's second largest coastal estuary, lies within the Seal Beach National Wildlife Refuge. Adjoining this refuge is the Seal Beach Naval Weapons Station, including the county's most biologically significant expanse of coastal terrace habitat west of the San Joaquin Hills.

The Los Angeles County line loosely follows the San Gabriel River and Coyote Creek channels inland for several miles. This part of the county is almost totally developed, with runoff carried south and west to the San Gabriel River via a series of rather depressing channels. Following the Coyote Creek channel north to Fullerton, we finally encounter coastal sage scrub and grasslands in the oil fields of the West Coyote Hills, with elevations ranging between approximately 300 and 500 feet. Tiny Laguna Lake lies to the northeast. East of Harbor Boulevard and Sunny Hills, in the Santa Ana River watershed, lies Brea Dam and the oil fields of the East Coyote Hills.

Heading up the Brea Canyon channel to the northeast, we encounter more oil fields in the Puente Hills, which barely extend into Orange County from Los Angeles and San Bernardino counties. Brea Canyon's eastern watersheds, including picturesque Tonner Canyon, drain the western slope of the steep, grassy Chino Hills. Carbon Canyon, including Sonome, Soquel and Telegraph canyons, drains portions of the Puente and Chino hills.

Perched on the San Bernardino County line south of Telegraph Canyon, San Juan Hill (1781 feet) marks the summit of the Chino Hills. Carbon Canyon Dam controls flows from Carbon Canyon before the water is channeled to the Santa Ana River. Yorba Linda Reservoir collects minor flows from oil fields on the coastal slope of the Chino Hills. The southeastern Chino Hills drain south to the Santa Ana River via Blue Mud (including Wire Springs Canyon), Box, Bee (including Lost Trough Canyon) and Brush canyons.

The impressive, east/west trending Santa Ana Canyon passes between the Chino Hills and the Santa Ana Mountains just south of Prado Dam, in the area where Orange, Riverside and San Bernardino counties meet. The river passes through linear Featherly Regional Park before feeding the Santa Ana River Lakes in east Anaheim. Entering the heart of Anaheim, the river bends south, with some of the water diverted into gravel pits. Then, in an 11-mile run through the cities of Anaheim, Santa Ana, Fountain Valley and Hunting-ton Beach, the "fully improved" channel first takes on the characteristics of a sandy beach, then is planted with turf for golf play, and is ultimately lined with concrete.

Upon reaching Talbert Regional Park in unincorporated county lands, the Santa Ana is again permitted a muddy bottom as it lumbers through tidal waters alongside two miles of remnant upland and brackish marsh ecosystems before spilling, mercifully, into the sparkling Pacific.

Habitat Descriptions

Orange County's native and naturalized terrestrial plants are adapted to life in a Mediterranean climate, growing during mild, moderately wet winters and springs, and tolerating hot, dry summers (or sitting them out as seeds). Riparian vegetation taps into underground aquifers and grows primarily during the warmer months of spring and summer. This section describes the county's major habitat types to provide a basic understanding of how vege-tation, water and other important aspects of the local environment affect bird distribution.

For purposes of describing habitats, and the distribution of birds in those habitats, the county is divided into three districts: District 1 (Ocean and Coast), District 2 (Lowlands and Lower Hills) and District 3 (Montane). Classification and nomenclature of plants follow Hickman (1993) and Roberts (1989). Scientific bird names are provided in the Appendix A checklist.

District 1 - Ocean and Coast

Habitat 1a consists of oceanic waters outside the kelp-line. Pelican Point, Dana Point and Newport Pier are favored spots for viewing species like Sooty and Black-vented shearwaters and Black Storm-Petrel, with occasional sightings of species such as Northern Fulmar, Ashy Storm-Petrel and Rhinoceros Auklet. On productive days, a diversity of pelagic species may be found farther from shore, particularly over major offshore topographic features like Lausen Knoll and Avalon Knoll. Species observed from boats with some regularity include Pink-footed Shearwater, Least Storm-Petrel, Arctic Tern, Sabine's Gull and Cassin's Auklet. Experienced offshore observer Richard R. Veit (in litt.) reports that a sewage outfall located approximately one mile off Huntington State Beach (apparently not visible from shore) "attracts hundreds of Mew Gulls, Bonaparte's Gulls, phalaropes, Horned Grebes, Black-vented Shearwaters." The true local status of many pelagic species remains to be discovered.

Habitat 1b covers the county's 42 miles of coastline and nearshore waters out to around the kelp-line. Dana Cove, the county's only natural, protected outer bay, was developed into Dana Harbor in the late 1960s. Other man-made harbors exist at Anaheim Bay, Sunset Aquatic Park, Huntington Harbour and Lower Newport Bay. In winter, these areas attract species such as Common Loon, Horned Grebe, Surf Scoter and Red-breasted Merganser. Orange County's famous sandy beaches extend from Seal Beach south to the Balboa Peninsula, and along the edge of the Capistrano Bight from Dana Point south to San Clemente. These beaches provide foraging habitat for species such as Sanderling and Marbled Godwit, and loafing areas for numerous gull species. During winter, Doheny Beach State Park hosts tremendous mixed gull flocks, and thousands of Bonaparte's Gulls commute several miles daily along the Santa Ana River channel between its mouth and a water treatment plant on Ellis Avenue. Two sandy areas near the mouth of the Santa Ana River channel (one on the beach and the other a short distance upstream) have been fenced and managed to provide nesting habitat for the California Least Tern, a once-common breeder nearly driven to extinction through pervasive disturbance of beaches. These same protected areas provide limited nesting opportunities for another declining beach nester, the federally threatened Western Snowy Plover. From Corona del Mar to Dana Point, the coastline is rocky and dramatic, providing a stretch of natural habitat for species like Pelagic and Brandt's cormorants, Wandering Tattler, Black Turnstone, Surfbird and, increasingly, Black Oystercatcher. Breakwaters and rock jetties strewn along the northern coast provide additional habitat for birds of the rocky coastline.

Coastal aquatic habitats, including estuaries, tidally influenced mouths of river channels, and salt and brackish marshes, comprise Habitat 1c. Until the early 1900s, almost unimaginable expanses of marshes and sloughs covered the lowlands between Anaheim Bay and Newport Bay, extending as far inland as Fountain Valley and Garden Grove. These biologically rich areas are now greatly reduced due to various "reclamation" projects, including massive drainage and fill operations, excavation of harbors and channelization of rivers. More or less natural estuarine areas are now found only at the Seal Beach National Wildlife Refuge (Anaheim Bay), Bolsa Chica and Upper Newport Bay. A strip of remnant intertidal wetlands exists along Pacific Coast Highway in Huntington Beach, and some fairly extensive wetlands have been created/enhanced near the mouth of the Santa Ana River channel. Common intertidal plants include California Cord Grass (*Spartina foliosa*), Eelgrass (*Zostera marina*), sea blight (*Suaeda* spp.), Alkali Heath (*Frankenia salina*) and pickleweed (*Salicornia* spp.). Species of the upper littoral zone include Emory Baccharis (*Baccharis emoryi*), Big Saltbush (*Atriplex lentiformis*) and Salt Grass (*Distichlis spicata*). Coastal estuaries, and even some degraded remnants, are some of the county's most important wildlife habitat areas, supporting resident and summering populations of numerous birds, including endangered species such as Light-footed Clapper Rail and Belding's Savannah Sparrow. Sandy, sparsely vegetated, man-made islands at Upper Newport Bay and Bolsa Chica support noisy, swirling flocks of nesting Black Skimmers and terns, including the endangered California Least Tern. Coastal estuaries serve as critical feeding and resting stations for large numbers of grebes, herons, egrets, ducks and shorebirds, and foraging areas for raptors like the Osprey and the endangered American Peregrine Falcon.

District 2 - Lowlands and Lower Hills (Below ~2000 Feet)

Habitat 2a includes freshwater marshes, lakes, reservoirs and river channels, and miscellaneous other transient aquatic habitats, such as vernal pools. The channelized Santa Ana River is the county's main watercourse, and man-made Irvine Lake is the largest reservoir. The only natural lakes in Orange County are the three hydrologically connected Laguna Lakes, located midway down Laguna Canyon. Allen (1984) reported that poorly studied vernal pools existed in Corona del Mar, El Toro and Dana Point prior to intensive development of these areas. This rare and biologically intriguing community was believed to have been eliminated from the county until the recent recognition of an extant vernal pool system at Fairview Park in Costa Mesa (others have been rumored near Irvine Lake and on Rancho Santa Margarita). A variety of migratory birds forage in Fairview Park's larger pools, including Snowy Egret, Mallard, American Wigeon, Greater Yellowlegs and Common Snipe. Extensive marshes and bogs existed along the county's major watercourses prior to mass settlement of flood-plains and attendant flood control activities. San Joaquin Marsh, adjacent to lower San Diego Creek, is the county's most important extant freshwater marsh. Typical emergent plants in our local marshes include cat-tail (*Typha* spp.), bulrush (*Scirpus* spp.), sedge (*Carex* spp.) and umbrella-sedge (*Cyperus* spp.). Willow (*Salix* spp.), Mulefat (*Baccharis salicifolia*) and other woody plants often grow around marsh edges (see Habitat 2b). Bird species that regularly nest at Orange County lakes, reservoirs and freshwater marshes include Pied-billed Grebe, Mallard, Cinnamon Teal, Ruddy Duck, American Coot, Black-necked Stilt, Black Phoebe and Red-winged Blackbird. A variety of herons, egrets, ducks, rails and shorebirds nest sporadically and/or in limited numbers at San Joaquin Marsh, Santa Ana River Lakes, the back ponds at Bolsa Chica, Big Canyon (adjacent to Upper Newport Bay) and at scattered smaller marshy areas. Western and Clark's Grebes nest at Oso Reservoir when the water level is high. In fall and winter, bird numbers at the county's freshwater marshes and water bodies swell with the passage and arrival of migratory shorebirds, ducks and geese from the north.

Habitat 2b includes low and middle elevation riparian areas, which support plant and animal communities that vary according to topography, elevation, soil conditions, water supply and degree of disturbance. A variable willow/mulefat scrub forms dense stands 10-25 feet tall along intermittent and perennial lowland streams and around the edges of marshy areas. Arroyo Willow (*Salix lasiolepis*) and Mulefat are typically present, often with other shrubby trees such as Mexican Elderberry (*Sambucus mexicana*) and Sandbar Willow (*S. exigua*); taller Black Willows (*S. gooddingii*) and Red Willows (*S. laevigata*) occasionally punctuate the canopy. Where water is plentiful and habitat is permitted to mature, willow forests develop. In Orange County, most lowland willow forests (the trees generally growing over 25 feet tall) are dominated by Black and Arroyo willows; Red Willow is locally dominant. Good examples of willow forest habitat are located in the flood control basins behind Villa Park, Brea and Bonita Canyon dams, along portions of San Diego Creek, at William R. Mason Regional Park and at scattered locations along the Santa Ana River. Cottonwood/willow forests, including towering Fremont and/or Black cottonwoods (*Populus fremontii, P. trichocarpa*), grow only in a few major lowland streams, including the upper Santa Ana River, Santiago Creek and portions of San Juan Creek. This community was, presumably, far more extensive in the county prior to channelization of our major streams. The graceful California Sycamore (*Platanus racemosa*) flourishes in washes and canyons, often growing in gravelly soil, alone or in association with other riparian woodland species. In the Arroyo

Trabuco and Bell Canyon, stands of White Alder (*Alnus rhombifolia*) extend downstream to approximately 500 and 1000 feet elevation, respectively; these areas provide nesting habitat for species like Western Wood-Pewee and Warbling Vireo that are found primarily in the mountains.

In District 2 riparian woodlands, the understory often includes herbaceous species like Mugwort (*Artemisia douglasiana*) and Western Ragweed (*Ambrosia psilostachya*). In relatively undisturbed stands, the understory typically includes thickets of native shrubs and vines like California Blackberry (*Rubus ursinus*) and California Rose (*Rosa californica*). Unfortunately, virtually all of the county's major streams have been subjected to biologically insensitive flood control practices, sand and gravel extraction operations, and other unnatural disturbances that facilitate establishment of invasive exotic plants. As a result, perennial weeds like Giant Reed (*Arundo donax*), pampas grass (*Cortaderia* spp.) and tamarisk (*Tamarix* spp.) have infested all of the county's major drainage systems. As a rule, these non-native plants provide poor quality nesting habitat for native birds; this is particularly true for endangered species like the Southwestern Willow Flycatcher and Least Bell's Vireo, which require extensive tangles of native riparian vegetation for nesting, foraging and cover.

Readers interested in viewing a broad spectrum of noxious weeds in one small area should visit Shipley Nature Center on the west side of Huntington Central Park. In "wild" Orange County, the unmanaged lower Santa Ana River open space south of Hamilton Avenue provides perhaps the most extreme example of invasion by exotic plants. There, impenetrable thickets of Selloa Pampas Grass (*Cortaderia selloana*), Giant Reed, Tree Tobacco (*Nicotiana glauca*), Castor-Bean (*Ricinus communis*), Five-hook Bassia (*Bassia hyssopifolia*) and Common Poison-Hemlock (*Conium maculatum*) have displaced numerous acres of native vegetation associated with the lower Santa Ana River.

More recently, sand and gravel operations in Santiago and lower Silverado canyons have facilitated a virtual explosion of Giant Reed in those riparian systems. The resource agencies responsible for maintaining the integrity of wetland ecosystems supposedly follow a policy requiring "no net loss of wetland habitat area *or value*." Yet, at the time this book goes to press, the U.S. Army Corps of Engineers proposes to issue a new "nationwide permit" authorizing "minimal regulation" of "discharges of dredged material incidental to active mining of sand and gravel" (Federal Register 61[117]:30785, 17 June 1996). Until these agencies, and society as a whole, show a credible interest in maintaining the *habitat value* of riparian systems and not just their size, the inexorable spread of invasive weeds will continue to represent the greatest threat to long-term viability of sensitive bird populations that nest along Orange County streams.

Widespread breeding birds associated with lowland riparian habitats include Black-chinned Hummingbird, House Wren, Common Yellowthroat, Song Sparrow, Brown-headed Cowbird, and Lesser and American goldfinches. Localized breeders include Downy Woodpecker, Tree Swallow, Swainson's Thrush, Yellow-breasted Chat, Blue Grosbeak and Lawrence's Goldfinch. The endangered Least Bell's Vireo, extirpated as a local breeder for decades, recolonized scattered lowland willow thickets in the county during the early 1990s.

Habitat 2c includes woodlands and riparian forests dominated by Coast Live Oak (*Quercus agrifolia*) and Southern California Black Walnut (*Juglans californica* var. *californica*); oak savannah and well developed oak landscaping are also included in this designation. Coast Live Oak woodlands occupy canyon bottoms in parts of District 2, and are also found on protected, north- and east-facing slopes (primarily in the interior foothills). The variable understory often includes flowering shrubs and shrubby trees such as Mexican Elderberry, Toyon (*Heteromeles arbutifolia*), Fuchsia-flowered Gooseberry (*Ribes speciosum*), Lemonade Berry (*Rhus integrifolia*), Heart-leaved Bush-Pentstemon (*Keckiella cordifolia*), Holly-leaved Redberry (*Rhamnus ilicifolia*) and Poison Oak (*Toxicodendron diversilobum*). The understory in oak savannah typically consists of predominantly non-native annual grasses such as brome (*Bromus* spp.) and wild oats (*Avena* spp.); where grazing and other disturbances have been minimal, prevalent native grasses include Purple Needlegrass (*Nasella pulchra*) and Small-flowered Melic Grass (*Melica imperfecta*). Walnut woodlands are found primarily in the Chino and Peralta hills. While the understory below these woodlands may include woody plants typical of oak woodlands, it is often sparse, consisting of herbaceous species like Chaparral Bedstraw (*Galium angustifolium* ssp. *angustifolium*) and Giant Wild Rye (*Leymus condensatus*). California Sycamores frequently occur with oaks and walnuts in riparian situations. Nesting bird species associated with these communities include Western Screech-Owl, Long-eared Owl (local and sporadic), Nuttall's and Acorn woodpeckers, Plain Titmouse, Hutton's Vireo, Orange-crowned Warbler and Bullock's Oriole.

Habitat 2d includes a variety of low, more or less open scrub associations that fall under the general heading of "coastal sage scrub;" foothill washes and lowland rocks, cliffs and bluffs are also included in this habitat classification. Coastal sage scrub consists of mostly drought-deciduous plants growing in well drained soils on slopes and bluffs. Dominant species in District 2 include California Sagebrush (*Artemisia californica*), California Buckwheat

(*Eriogonum fasciculatum* ssp. *fasciculatum*), White Sage (*Salvia apiana*), Black Sage (*S. mellifera*), Buff Monkeyflower (*Mimulus aurantiacus*), prickly-pear (*Opuntia* spp.) and Coastal Cholla (*O. prolifera*); Big Saltbush is locally dominant near the coast. The federally threatened Coastal California Gnatcatcher particularly favors scrub along seasonal drainage courses and on relatively gentle slopes near the coast. In scrub containing significant patches of cactus, the Cactus Wren's guttural chatter resonates through the hills. The retiring Southern California Rufous-crowned Sparrow shows a preference for steep, grassy ecotonal areas. More widespread species include California Quail, Greater Roadrunner, Costa's Hummingbird, Bewick's Wren and California Towhee; wintering White-crowned Sparrows are abundant and widespread, while Golden-crowned Sparrows stick mostly to relatively moist scrub and chaparral of the foothills and mountains. Lesser Nighthawks nest locally in and around foothill washes, and particularly rocky areas attract limited numbers of Rock and Canyon wrens.

Habitat 2e includes maritime, southern mixed, and middle elevation chaparral, diverse assemblages containing primarily evergreen, sclerophyllous shrubs that grow denser and taller than coastal sage scrub. In Orange County, maritime chaparral grows up to approximately 1000 feet elevation in the vicinity of South Laguna, including Niguel Hill and Aliso Canyon; several plants reach their northern limits in these areas. Characteristic species include Bushrue (*Cnemoridium dumosum*), Coastal Scrub Oak (*Quercus dumosa*), Chamise (*Adenostema fasciculatum*), Southern Summer Holly (*Comarostaphylis diversifolia* ssp. *diversifolia*), Coastal Prickly-Pear (*Opuntia littoralis*) and Greenbark Ceanothus (*Ceanothus spinosus*). Southern mixed chaparral also grows at low elevations near the coast but is more widely distributed than maritime chaparral; it is most common in the canyons of the San Joaquin Hills. Dominant species include Toyon, Laurel Sumac (*Malosma laurina*), Lemonade Berry, California Scrub Oak (*Q. berberidifolia*) and, locally, Coastal Scrub Oak. Middle elevation chaparral is a generalized community that grows between approximately 1000 and 3000 feet elevation (overlapping somewhat with high elevation chaparral associations). This community covers large areas of the lower Santa Ana Mountains and portions of the lower hills. Middle elevation chaparral dominants include Chamise, Bigpod Ceanothus (*C. megacarpus*), Sugarbush (*Rhus ovata*), Holly-leaved Redberry and Whipple's Yucca (*Yucca whipplei*). Although the county's chaparral communities differ floristically and elevationally, they support a fairly uniform assortment of bird species. Residents include Western Scrub-Jay, Wrentit, California Thrasher and Spotted Towhee; the migratory Blue-gray Gnatcatcher nests locally. Wintering species include Hermit Thrush, Yellow-rumped Warbler, Golden-crowned and Fox sparrows.

Habitat 2f includes grasslands, rangelands, athletic fields, agricultural fields, ruderal (weedy) areas, and other similarly open situations. As a result of over-grazing and other abusive agricultural practices, the vast majority of Orange County's remaining grasslands contain primarily non-native, annual grasses and ruderal forbs. However, significant stands of native bunchgrasses and annual wildflowers can still be found. Most of our remaining native grass-lands are dominated by needlegrass (*Nasella* spp.) set among other grasses and vivid sprays of wildflowers. The county's most expansive native grass-lands occupy the southern table lands inland from San Juan Capistrano and San Clemente; significant pockets also exist within the Chino Hills and San Joaquin Hills, on Loma Ridge and in the Santa Ana Mountains. Non-native grasslands are dominated by annual grasses such as bromes, wild oats and barley (*Hordeum* spp.), along with ruderal forbs such as mustard (*Brassica* spp., *Hirschfeldia geniculata*), filarees (*Erodium* spp.) and Fascicled Tarplant (*Hemizonia fasciculatum*); highly disturbed grasslands often include partic-ularly nasty weeds such as Cardoon (*Cynara cardunculus*), Russian-thistle (*Salsola tragus*) and Yellow Star-thistle (*Centaurea solstitialis*). Weedy lots and disturbed slopes support stands of tall ruderal forbs such as Castor-Bean and Sweet Fennel (*Foeniculum vulgare*). Although comprised largely of non-native plants, Habitat 2f supports a wide variety of resident, summering and wintering birds, including several species of raptor and sparrow, Canada Goose, Western Kingbird, California Horned Lark and Western Meadowlark. The vast, secluded fields of the Seal Beach Naval Weapons Station support remarkable raptor concentrations, including several pairs of the rare Western Burrowing Owl, a species once ubiquitous to grasslands and rangelands of the county and region. Until its recent destruction, the expansive Plano Trabuco regularly hosted wintering flocks of longspurs, including Chestnut-collareds by the dozen, a few Laplands and, rarely, McCown's.

The remaining lowlands, including developed parks, residential yards, golf courses, orchards, dumps and urban areas, are grouped as Habitat 2g. This habitat supports its own complement of resident birds that are generally tolerant of humans, some to the point of cheekiness. Familiar faces include those of Anna's Hummingbird, Black Phoebe, American Crow, Bushtit, Northern Mockingbird, American Robin, House Finch and Hooded Oriole. Introduced residents include Rock and Spotted doves, European Starling and House Sparrow, while boisterous flocks of colorful exotic parrots and para-keets lend a tropical flair to many Orange County neighborhoods. Winter-ing native species include Hermit Thrush, Yellow-rumped Warbler, Cedar Waxwing and White-crowned Sparrow. Birding's preeminent phenomenon in recent decades has been the explosion of records pertaining to "vagrants" (species out of their normal range), and local birders have certainly placed tiny Orange County on the map in this respect. A handful of "hard-cores" have been particularly productive, relentlessly combing carefully selected portions of Habitat 2g in search of lost travelers. During spring and fall migration periods, birds and birders seek out local "migrant traps" that typically feature tall trees, dense underbrush and water. The best of these are located near the coast, although inland locations may be productive during spring and late fall/winter. Huntington Central Park, the county's top spot for migrant songbirds, has hosted approximately 270 native species to date, including eye-poppers like Mississippi Kite, Sulphur-bellied Flycatcher, Sedge Wren, White-eyed Vireo (two in spring), Yellow-throated Vireo (three in spring, two in fall), Blue-winged Warbler, Louisiana Waterthrush and Field Sparrow. While Irvine Regional Park is a worthwhile birding destination any time of the year, it is best known for late fall and winter vagrants like Barrow's Goldeneye, Zone-tailed Hawk, Yellow-bellied Sapsucker, Chestnut-sided Warbler, Clay-colored, Field and Harris' sparrows, and Scott's Oriole. Several other consistently productive areas are known, and many more remain to be discovered and adopted by enthusiastic birders; this is especially true in the south county, where observer coverage remains remarkably light.

As development claims more natural areas in Orange County and beyond, migratory birds increasingly depend on variations on the "managed landscape" for food and cover between distant nesting and wintering grounds. As such, birders can help migratory bird populations by working with governmental agencies to improve habitat conditions in parks and areas adjacent to human developments. For example, prolonged education and lobbying efforts by birders led to improved landscape management practices in portions of Huntington Central Park, including reduced tree and understory pruning, preservation of downed trunks and limbs, and increased tolerance of weedy patches. Ongoing native plant community restoration projects include Sea & Sage Audubon Society's chaparral and oak woodland plantings at Irvine Regional Park, and the California Native Plant Society's coastal bluff scrub restoration program at Fairview Park in Costa Mesa.

District 3 - Mountains (~2000 Feet and Higher)

Habitat 3a includes upper riparian woodlands growing in moist, narrow canyons of the Santa Ana Mountains. Characteristic tree species include Big-leaf Maple (*Acer macrophyllum*), White Alder, California Bay (*Umbellularia californica*), Coast Live Oak and California Sycamore. The mature canopy may reach over 100 feet tall above a rich understory of dense saplings, chaparral shrubs and tangles of species like California Blackberry and Wild Grape (*Vitis girdiana*). In and around human outposts, Blue Periwinkle (*Vinca major*), Edible Fig (*Ficus carica*) and other exotics have invaded numerous streambeds and hillsides, displacing native species that many birds require for nesting and foraging. Regular summer residents include Pacific-slope Flycatcher, Western Wood-Pewee, Swainson's Thrush (local), Warbling Vireo (local), Orange-crowned Warbler, Yellow Warbler (local) and Black-headed Grosbeak. Within District 3, passage of migratory landbirds is largely concentrated in riparian and mixed oak/coniferous forest habitats of the highest canyons. Limited data suggest that fall migrants and winter visitors with montane affinities (e.g., Red-breasted Nuthatch, Ruby-crowned Kinglet, Townsend's Warbler, Hermit Warbler) tend to arrive earlier in the upper Santa Ana Mountains than in the foothills and lowlands. Expansive and readily accessible examples of higher elevation riparian woodlands exist in Trabuco, Holy Jim, Harding, Silverado and San Juan canyons.

Habitat 3b, mixed oak/coniferous forest, consists of Big-cone Douglas-fir (*Pseudotsuga macrocarpa*) and Coulter Pine (*Pinus coulteri*) mixed with Canyon Live Oak (*Quercus chrysolepis*) and, locally, Knobcone Pine (*P. attenuata*). This stately community grows only in protected portions of the highest mountains, with the most extensive stands occurring in upper Trabuco Canyon. Other locations include Silverado, Harding, Santiago, Bell and Hot Springs canyons. These remote, poorly studied forests support limited nesting populations of some of the county's rarest denizens, including California Spotted Owl, Northern Saw-Whet Owl, Hairy Woodpecker, Olive-sided Flycatcher, Mountain Chickadee and Western Tanager. Several additional species formerly known or presumed to nest in the county's oak/coniferous forests have not been found in recent decades; thus, these beautiful, remote areas represent an intriguing frontier for intrepid birders.

Habitat 3c includes high elevation chaparral, high elevation coastal sage scrub, Tecate Cypress (*Cupressus forbesii*) forest and high elevation cliffs. Chaparral communities occurring in District 3 are dominated by species such as Chamise, manzanita (*Arctostaphylos* spp.), Hoary-leaved Ceanothus (*Ceanothus crassifolius*), Birch-leaf Mountain Mahogany (*Cercocarpus betuloides* var. *betuloides*) and Interior Live Oak (*Quercus wislizenii*). Coastal sage scrub in District 3 is characterized by open stands of White Sage, California Sagebrush, California Buckwheat, Whipple's Yucca and Laurel Sumac. Tecate Cypress forest, found in the upper portions of Coal, Gypsum and Fremont canyons, is characterized by extremely dense stands of Tecate Cypress. Species that regularly nest in these communities include Mountain Quail, Common Poorwill, Blue-gray Gnatcatcher and Black-chinned Sparrow. High elevation cliffs provide nesting habitat for White-throated Swifts, Violet-green Swallows and many raptors, including Turkey Vultures, Golden Eagles and, perhaps, Prairie Falcons.

Avian Population Trends

Bird populations, like those of all living organisms, exist in a state of flux, rising and falling in response to environmental conditions. A short list of important variables includes pressures exerted by other organisms (e.g., competition for food and cover, predator/prey interactions, outbreaks of disease), cyclic weather patterns (e.g., periods of drought, periodic warming of ocean waters), long-term climatic trends (e.g., "global warming"), catastrophic events (e.g., fires, major storms), and habitat modification (i.e., destruction, creation, degradation, enhancement and fragmentation). The myriad factors affecting plant and wildlife populations interrelate, and their sum effect determines whether a given population increases, decreases or remains relatively constant during a selected period of time. Direct and indirect effects of human actions, both positive and negative, modify baseline conditions under which plants and wildlife find equilibrium, and the additive effects of human actions may alter ecological relationships unpredictably.

Over the past century, radical changes in the southern California landscape, particularly habitat destruction and the widespread establishment of exotic plant and animal populations, have led to extirpation and decline of numerous native plant and wildlife populations. While there is good reason to celebrate the continued survival of endangered species like the American Peregrine Falcon and California Least Tern, it is important to recognize that these graceful predators have ceased to symbolize functioning ecosystems, existing here only through intensive human management of their remnant populations. As Orange County contemplates yet another period of rapid growth, it would be refreshing for local decision-makers to bear in mind the many native species already evicted from here, and the precarious status of many localized and declining plant and wildlife populations.

This overview focuses on trends visible in the county's bird populations, emphasizing the past 20 years. The first part considers oceanic species, whose status in Orange County is generally beyond local human control. The lengthier second part focuses on terrestrial and estuarine species, and ways that local land use decisions and management actions affect their Orange County populations.

Birds of the Offshore Waters

Orange County's restricted offshore area relative to San Diego and Los Angeles counties has served to limit birder interest in exploring pelagic waters between Orange County ports and Santa Catalina Island. Most direct knowledge of the local status of oceanic birds derives from observations made by a small group of birders who regularly gaze seaward from shore. While coverage of the local offshore waters has improved in recent years, the status of species that typically remain far offshore is still largely inferred from data gathered elsewhere in southern California.

Since Orange County does not support any seabird nesting colonies, variations in the bird life observed off our coast typically result from a combination of 1) population dynamics at more or less distant nesting colonies, 2) climatic factors, particularly those affecting ocean water temperatures, and 3) large-scale human effects such as oil spills and depletion of fish stocks. For example, a near lack of Common Murre sightings in Orange County since 1984 has coincided with crashes of murre breeding colonies in central California and Washington. Takekawa et al. (1990) and Ainley et al. (1994) documented these declines and attributed them to the combined effects of oil spills, capture of murres in gill-nets, and reduced availability of fish prey species due to a far reaching "El Niño" (warm ocean water) condition in 1982/83. Readers interested in learning about factors affecting the occurrence of birds off the California coast are referred to Briggs et al. (1987) as a start.

A 1992 El Niño condition experienced as far north as British Columbia resulted in, or at least catalyzed, unprecedented influxes of normally pelagic species to nearshore waters in Orange County and many other places. As many as 30,000 Black-vented Shearwaters, normally scarce or absent during the summer months, swarmed off Newport Beach during June and July 1992. At least 100 Pink-footed Shearwaters observed from Newport Pier 21 July 1992 exceeded typical high daily counts by an order of magnitude. Storm-petrels visible from piers and points of land included Black, Ashy and even the elusive Least. The spread of warm ocean waters from the south also encouraged a minor incursion of Masked and Brown boobies to California during the summer of 1992, including an immature Masked observed briefly from Newport Pier on 30 June 1992. While warm ocean waters certainly played a central role in these remarkable events, Richard R. Veit (in litt.) warns that the connection between El Niño and observable changes in bird populations "is not as clear cut as is usually described." For example, Veit's CALCOFI research cruises off the coast of California noted higher numbers of two southern species, Brown Pelican and Heermann's Gull, in 1991, not 1992. We strongly encourage readers to help fill gaps in our knowledge of Orange County's offshore waters.

Birds of Upland, Riparian and Estuarine Ecosystems

Over the past century, most of Orange County's coastal lowlands have been filled, channelized, flattened, paved, built up or converted to intensive agricultural production. The bulk of destructive activities, including streambed channelization, wetland "reclamation" and encroachment into floodplains, occurred prior to 1960, when open spaces were plentiful, ecological awareness was low, and intensive development projects were almost universally viewed as beneficial. Vast tracts of land in northern and western portions of the county were converted to a poorly differentiated mass of faceless cities devoid of natural features. During this era, only a few visionaries nationwide recognized the "hidden" ecological and human costs associated with unplanned, unregulated development of natural areas.

Sleeper (1986) reported that the following mammals have been extirpated from Orange County within the past 100 years: Tule Elk (*Cervus elaphus nannodes*), Grizzly Bear (*Ursus chelan*)[1], Pronghorn Antelope (*Antilocapra americana*), and perhaps Gray Wolf (*Canis lupus*). The very limited historic range of Pacific Pocket Mouse (*Perognathus longimembris pacificus*), a species of the coastal strand, alluvium and marine terrace deposits, is centered in Orange County (Hall 1981). This tiny rodent was feared extinct until a tiny remnant population was rediscovered at the Dana Point Headlands in 1993 (additional small populations have subsequently been found in northern coastal San Diego County). Among birds, the last Orange County sighting of a California Condor occurred in 1940; this magnificent bird was ultimately removed from the wild altogether (then subsequently reintroduced) after a combination of shooting, egg collection, poisoning, power line collisions and habitat loss reduced the population to just a few individuals. By the middle of the century, ornithologists had noted regional declines in species such as the Southern Bald Eagle, California Least Tern, Western Burrowing Owl, Light-footed Clapper Rail, Western Yellow-billed Cuckoo and Least Bell's Vireo; serious scientific studies, planning policies and management measures were not enacted, however, until the federal Endangered Species and Clean Water acts of the 1970s, when many more species were imperiled. Enforcement of these landmark policies, including design and implementation of intensive recovery programs, permitted many

---

[1]Sleeper (1986) reported that California's last authenticated specimen was shot in San Mateo Canyon in 1899, but Storer and Tevis (1955) noted a skin and skull taken at Trabuco Canyon in January 1908 (#US National Museum 156594), and Pequegnat (1951 p. 46) received first-hand accounts that "the last [Orange County] specimen was observed on the west face of Santiago Peak in the fall of 1908." Finally, Garrett (1993 p.80) includes a photograph of a hunter standing over a giant female shot in Tujunga Canyon (Los Angeles County) in 1916, "the last documented record of a Grizzly Bear in southern California."

wetland-dependent species to persist and even expand their numbers in the county and region. Major land set-asides and management programs are now being considered and implemented, with the goal of conserving species associated with coastal sage scrub and other selected upland communities. This section examines past and present avian population trends evident in Orange County's major onshore ecosystems.

Upland Birds

Since the late 1800s, Orange County's coastal plain and lower hills have been subjected to ever-increasing development pressures from agriculture, oil exploration, and residential, commercial and industrial development. Since in the mid-1970s, residential/commercial development has been euphemistically characterized as "master planned." Until very recently, however, the near absence of ecologically based planning within the county and region has yielded large-scale destruction, fragmentation and degradation of native plant and animal communities, with a concomitant lowering of the quality of life for human inhabitants.

While native upland biotic communities throughout the region have suffered adverse effects, attention has focused on coastal sage scrub, coastal bluff scrub and maritime chaparral, natural communities with limited global distributions that support many resident species incapable of surviving elsewhere. Progressive concern from researchers, policy makers and the public led to federal listing of the Coastal California Gnatcatcher as a threatened species in 1993, which in turn propelled development of the Natural Communities Conservation Planning (NCCP) process. The NCCP is a cooperative program involving federal, state and local governmental agencies, and private land owners with the goal of accomplishing scientifically based regional open space planning in areas that support expanses of coastal sage scrub. In addition to the gnatcatcher, declining resident bird species associated with coastal sage scrub include Greater Roadrunner, Cactus Wren, Bell's Sage Sparrow and Southern California Rufous-crowned Sparrow.

Although less significant on a global scale, a combination of development activities and adaptation of intensive agricultural practices has precipitated local declines in nesting or wintering populations of an even greater number of grassland-dependent bird species. These include White-tailed Kite, Northern Harrier, Swainson's Hawk, Ferruginous Hawk, Rough-legged Hawk, Prairie Falcon, Mountain Plover, Western Burrowing Owl, California Horned Lark, Grasshopper Sparrow, Vesper Sparrow and Chestnut-collared Longspur. Since the primary goal of the NCCP program is the conservation of coastal sage scrub resources, we may expect continued local declines of grassland-dependent species as the remaining flatlands are preferentially sacrificed to development.

Benefitting from liberal distributions in the Cleveland National Forest and other large wilderness areas, and often growing in steep canyons and on higher elevation slopes that are not easily built upon, chaparral, oak woodlands and coniferous forests have fared better than other communities in the push to settle Orange County. Nonetheless, populations of several migratory passerines appear to be extirpated or seriously declining in our local mountains. For example, the local breeding population of Hermit Thrush now seems to be extirpated from the Santa Ana Mountains, and perhaps one Purple Martin pair remains in the county. Cassin's Solitary Vireo and Black-throated Gray Warbler probably nested in the Santa Anas historically (cf. Pequegnat 1951, S&H 1979), but almost certainly do not now. S&H (1979) suspected that "preemption of nest sites by Starlings...reduced the martin nesting population," but the general scarcity of starlings in the higher mountain canyons, where Purple Martins nested through at least 1988, suggests that other factors are involved. The same principal applies to the Brown-headed Cowbird, another deleterious species whose numbers are reduced in the mountains compared with the foothills and lowlands.

Johnson (1994) postulated that recent, predominantly northward and westward extensions of the breeding ranges of several bird species may be linked to a decades-long trend in the western U.S. toward increased summer moisture and, perhaps, increased summer temperature. He cautioned, however, that "some distributional 'expansions'...may actually be range *shifts* in which regions are evacuated in one part of the distribution as a wave of colonization advances elsewhere" (p. 38; his emphasis). The migratory passerine species declining in Orange County's protected mountain canyons were not listed by Johnson among those extending their ranges elsewhere in the West (Solitary Vireo's range expansion pertains to the Plumbeous race originally of the Rocky Mountains), and it bears noting that climatic factors that may favor distributional "expansions" or "shifts" for some species may contribute to *range contractions* in others.

If the adverse trend described above continues, local breeding populations at greatest risk include those of the Olive-sided Flycatcher, Swainson's Thrush, Warbling Vireo, California Yellow Warbler and Western Tanager. In addition to these scarce summer residents, rare and/or localized permanent residents of the Santa Ana Mountains include the Golden Eagle, California Spotted Owl, Long-eared Owl and Northern Saw-whet Owl, Hairy Woodpecker, Mountain Chickadee and Bell's Sage Sparrow. With the passing of time, some of these species may also prove susceptible to local extirpation.

Wetland-dependent Birds

Few living Orange County residents can recall, and relatively few have been informed of, the natural condition of the coastal lowlands northwest of Newport Bay, an area known as the Gospel Swamp less than a century ago. In 1769, Gaspar de Portolá is reported to have found the Santa Ana River "a foot deep and a half mile wide in *July*" (Sleeper 1982 p. 59, his emphasis). According to the same source (p. 59), "in 1890 the State Geologist estimated that 10,000 acres of [peat] west of the river ran anywhere from three to thirty feet deep." Writing in the early 1950s, county pioneer Thomas B. Talbert (1982 p. 37) provided the following vivid description of this wetland system:

> *Originally, except for the Huntington Beach Mesa, the coastal area extending from the Newport Mesa to the Bolsa Chica Mesa and back into the country as far as Bolsa, a distance of about 7.5 miles, was considered a practically worthless swamp. This area of about 30 square miles, 8000 acres, was so full of peat springs and artesian wells which flowed the year around that it was quite inaccessible. It had a growth of willows, sycamores, tules, water moodies, wild blackberry and other vines, grasses and shrubs that made an almost impenetrable thicket... Besides being a refuge for wild ducks, geese and birds, it housed many wildcats, coons, wild hogs, coyotes, badgers, and even black diamond rattlesnakes, which usually floated in on the flood waters.*

According to Sleeper (1982 pp. 59-60), extensive alluvial wetlands were not limited to the Santa Ana River's western flank.

> *East of the river, between it and the hills of the Lomas [de Santiago], lay another vast moor. Running from Red Hill to Newport's back bay, the Spanish called it "La cienega de las ranas" - roughly "Frog Swamp." Undrained and untilled until the late 'seventies [1870s], the soil's productivity on both sides of the Santa Ana was staggering.*

Fantastic descriptions of waterfowl numbers and hunting opportunities provide the most compelling written accounts of local bird life in the early years. Again, Talbert (1982 p. 40) provided a stirring reminiscence:

> *This section of the country along the coast between Long Beach and Newport Beach, south of Westminster, was one of the greatest natural habitats for wild life and game birds in the world. Wild ducks, geese, jack-snipe, coots, plover, doves, killdeer, egrets, herons, gulls, pelicans, land birds, and waterfowl of every kind and description varied their flights from ocean to swamp, from swamp*

to grain fields, from grain fields to ocean again, to feast on
seafood, grain, seeds, bugs, toads, worms, grasshoppers, and the
like. I have seen birds by the thousands so thick in flight as to
almost eclipse the sun. The hours-long flight of ducks patterned
against a blazing sunset was most amazingly spectacular and beau-
tiful. When startled, great flocks of birds arose to circle around and
return to their beloved haven.

Bolstering the credibility of Talbert's recollection, Grinnell (1898) described
"immense numbers" of wintering Snow Geese that caused "considerable
damage to grain and alfalfa crops" by day, spending the night "out at sea
resting on the water in large beds a few miles off shore along with swarms
of ducks." Not surprisingly, numerous private duck clubs arose in Orange
County in the early 1900s, serving mostly "wealthy Los Angeles men who
sometimes shot more than the limit of 25 ducks a day and often did not
bother to pick them up off the ground" (Lee 1973 p. 67).

Sleeper (1973 p. 221) suggested that a comparative scarcity of game was
evident by the late 1800s, recounting Santa Ana *Standard* editor Dan M.
Baker's 1895 complaint that "last week four Los Angeles sportsmen, following a two day hunt...left with [only] 900 geese for the city markets;" this
compared to the "*old days*, when hundreds of hunters in the region could get
over 200 geese a day" (his emphasis). A photograph on file at the First
American Title Insurance Company in Santa Ana documents the 1901
slaughter of approximately 100 geese by a man and boy in Santiago Canyon.
Most are Aleutian and Cackling Canada Geese, with approximately ten
Snow (and possibly Ross') Geese. The federally threatened Aleutian
Canada Goose is otherwise unrecorded in the county. Willett (1933 p. 28)
chronicled major declines in the region's wintering waterfowl populations
due to intensive market and recreational hunting, as well as crop protection,
and foresaw their continued downward spiral in the absence of conservation
measures:

> *The geese have probably suffered more at the hands of man than*
> *any other of our California game birds... Only a fraction of former*
> *numbers remains and this is growing smaller yearly. Unless better*
> *protection is afforded and more feeding and resting grounds*
> *provided, geese will soon be numbered among the rarities of our*
> *avifauna.*

As excessive as the losses to hunting were, far more of Orange County's bird
populations have suffered extirpation or major decline as a result of habitat
destruction and degradation, particularly the draining of the Gospel Swamp
and channelization of the Santa Ana River. In Talbert's (1982 pp. 58-64)

view, "the vital problem [before the turn of the century] was to get enough water drained off the land so it could be cleared and made productive." Having participated in the massive undertaking to dig the needed canals, Talbert recalled, "the drainage revealed some of the richest soil in the world. Corn! Potatoes! Pumpkins! My! How they did grow." However, "the next problem was to confine the river to a definite location to protect the valley from this hazard," and in 1900 Talbert and others "organized and incorporated the Newbert River Protection District [which] comprised about 18,000 acres extending from Santa Ana...to the north, to Garden Grove and Huntington Beach on the south, and the Costa Mesa Bluffs on the east." Using $185,000 in public bonds, the District "bought a 300 foot strip for a permanent river-bed, dredged a channel, and built levees to hold the Santa Ana River where it is located at the present time." Recalling all of this around 1950, Talbert was moved to marvel, "looking at the valley, now one of the richest farming areas in the world, you never could believe that such a change could come to pass in one man's span of life."

In subsequent decades, the rich alluvial farmlands of the Santa Ana River floodplain were paved over and converted to residential neighborhoods and strip malls. The channel was subsequently paved and lined with rip-rap, at public expense, to protect streets and structures built in areas naturally predisposed to flooding. The biological toll of these actions encompasses much more than the mighty swarms of waterfowl described by Talbert and Grinnell, and would be useless to calculate. Insectivores were surely hit hard; those known or presumed to have nested in and around the Gospel Swamp/Santa Ana River ecosystem include such troubled species as Western Yellow-billed Cuckoo, Southwestern Willow Flycatcher, Bank Swallow, Least Bells' Vireo, California Yellow Warbler and Wilson's Warbler. Every day, tens of thousands of commuters on Orange County freeways bear witness to the massive, irreversible degradation of the Santa Ana River. Knowing the river's glorious past, who can gaze upon the sterile flood control channel's concrete and sand without feeling regret and shame?

Although Orange County has lost significant wetland resources, roughly two decades of federal and state resource management policies mandating the preservation, restoration and, in some cases, aggressive management of estuarine and riparian communities have essentially stabilized the county's wetland-dependent bird populations compared with the situation 20 years ago. Man-made islands at Bolsa Chica and Upper Newport Bay have attracted nesting colonies of Black Skimmer and several tern species (see Collins et al. 1991). The Seal Beach National Wildlife Refuge (Anaheim Bay) supports the county's largest California Least Tern population and a major Light-footed Clapper Rail population. At Bolsa Chica, small numbers of Western Snowy Plovers (the county's main nesting population) are over-shadowed by the west coast's northernmost major Elegant Tern and Black Skimmer nesting colonies, together with Caspian, Royal, Forster's and California Least terns. In 1995, these were joined for a short time by two Gull-billed Terns, the county's first, which unfortunately did not remain to nest. Two fenced nesting areas near the mouth of the Santa Ana River provide important nesting opportunities for California Least Terns and up to a few pairs of Western Snowy Plovers. Forster's and California Least terns and Black Skimmers nest at Upper Newport Bay, near broad expanses of cord-grass and pickleweed that support the nation's largest remaining population of Light-footed Clapper Rails.

The rapid settlement of Orange County by swarms of terns and skimmers has perhaps drawn attention away from modest signs of resurgence made by several other species that nest locally in and around protected estuaries and marshes. Unexpected and exciting was the 1991 discovery of an active American Peregrine Falcon nest site along the coast. Double-crested Cor-morants and Great and Snowy egrets have nested in small numbers at the Santa Ana River Lakes during the 1990s, and a pair of Great Egrets was found nesting at Irvine Lake in 1992. Following the wet winter of 1992/93, summer yielded a variety of nesting ducks unprecedented in recent times. Multiple broods of Northern Pintail, Blue-winged Teal, Gadwall and Redhead were found in the back ponds of Bolsa Chica, with broods of the last two species also found at San Joaquin Marsh. The presence of approx-imately 120 Gadwall at Bolsa Chica in June 1995 suggests that a major status change is under way for this species. Common Moorhens nest at several locations, and small numbers of Soras and Virginia Rails apparently nest in the county, at least sporadically. If agreement is possible among the many parties involved in the management of San Joaquin Marsh, imple-mentation of a thoughtful and comprehensive marsh master plan could solidify future prospects for many marsh denizens.

Among wintering birds, American White Pelican flocks numbering in the hundreds have become commonplace along the upper Santa Ana River since 1988/89. Several species of gull, including Herring, Western and Glaucous-winged, which were quite rare inland as recently as ten years ago, now regu-larly exploit Orange County landfills, reservoirs and the upper Santa Ana River. This increased utilization of inland resources is consistent with ongoing changes in the winter ranges of many gull species throughout the West, as doc-umented and discussed by Binford and Johnson (1995).

Among passerines, the most encouraging development must be the growing numbers of endangered Least Bell's Vireos that have nested in scattered lowland willow woodlands each year since 1991, after an absence of decades.

In the coastal lowlands, limited numbers of Swainson's Thrushes, Yellow-breasted Chats and Blue Grosbeaks continue to nest locally, where habitat conditions permit. In periodic fits of optimism, we look forward to the day when nesting Southwestern Willow Flycatchers may again grace our lowland riparian woodlands. In the foothills and mountains, small populations of Swainson's Thrush, Warbling Vireo and California Yellow Warbler persist locally where dense riparian forests remain. As discussed previously, long-term climatic changes may have more profound effects on local breeding populations of these migratory passerines than human activities, at least in the higher mountains.

In addition to habitat degradation by exotic plants, major threats remain for wetland-dependent bird populations in the form of non-native wildlife species that have colonized the region with man's assistance. The introduced Red Fox (*Vulpes vulpes*) is currently resident at Mile Square Park (where they are *fed*), Seal Beach National Wildlife Refuge and along inland portions of the Santa Ana River, with occasional sightings at other locales, including Bolsa Chica and Upper Newport Bay. Red Fox depredation threatens breeding populations of numerous estuarine species, including Light-footed Clapper Rail, terns, Black Skimmer and Belding's Savannah Sparrow (Lewis et al. 1993, Zembal 1993). Passerines nesting in riparian habitats are plagued by the Brown-headed Cowbird, an efficient nest parasite whose numbers have been tremendously augmented throughout the West by various human modifications of the natural landscape (Rothstein 1994). Aggressive management of Red Fox and Brown-headed Cowbird will be essential to the viability of many of the county's most sensitive bird populations into the foreseeable future.

Conclusion

As alluded to previously, Thomas B. Talbert played instrumental roles in a remarkable array of seminal development activities in coastal Orange County. These included drainage of Gospel Swamp, channelization of the Santa Ana River, condemnation of lands for construction of Pacific Coast Highway, making arrangements for the first oil lease in Huntington Beach, and development of Newport Harbor. In his time, Talbert was widely considered a visionary, and his sentiments remain close to the hearts of many contemporary bureaucrats, politicians and other opinion leaders in Orange County.

Talbert's memoirs from the early 1950s (published in 1982) provide disturbing insight into a mind that seemed to revel in nature's extravagant wonders, yet readily dismissed as "worthless" the natural systems that quite obviously produced such impressive bounty. His book, which may be found at the Mariners Branch of the Newport Beach Public Library, is recommended to anyone interested in examining the attitudes that have "developed" and homogenized most of lowland Orange County's lush and varied natural landscape in just three generations. In the final chapter, entitled "Looking Forward to the Next Sixty Years," Talbert anticipated the day when Huntington Beach would be "built into a substantial and prosperous metropolitan area of 50,000 people in a very short time, [perhaps even surpassing] the phenomenal growth of Long Beach" (p. 118). In the name of "good business," Talbert implored his fellow citizens to build a small municipal airport adjacent to the state beach on land "useless and without value because it is covered with swamps, pickleweed, and mud flats that would bog a jacksnipe... One important result would be the forcing of drainage necessary for the airport, thereby bringing about the drainage of the whole coastal area recently annexed into the City of Huntington Beach" (p. 120). The chapter closes with a disingenuous homily that should sound familiar to Orange County residents: "Blessed as we are with a wealth of natural resources, we should lay aside our petty greed and work in harmony for the growth of the thriving, prosperous community that Huntington Beach has the right to be, and which it certainly is destined to be if each person does what he should."

Although the airport idea foundered, the people of Huntington Beach (population 182,000 in 1990) and surrounding areas otherwise followed Talbert's instructions obediently. The streambeds were channelized, thousands of acres of marshlands were filled, and the rich farmlands were rapidly converted to roads, sidewalks and structures. In just four generations, the magnificent natural conditions that developed in coastal Orange County over the course of millenia have been degraded so radically and permanently that future generations will have great difficulty even imagining the rich natural heritage that should have been theirs.

As this book goes to press, the Eastern and San Joaquin Hills transportation corridors are plowing through undeveloped portions of the northern Santa Ana Mountains, Loma Ridge, and the San Joaquin Hills. In addition to direct damages from their construction, these toll roads will open some of Orange County's last expansive open spaces to large-scale residential and commercial development. Southerly extensions of the Foothill Transportation Corridor and Antonio Parkway, and accompanying developments, threaten to wreak similar damage in the pastoral southern foothills and ranch lands. Concurrently, one NCCP conservation plan has been adopted, and another is under development. When completed, these NCCP plans will 1) set the final boundaries for Orange County's primary natural open spaces in the lowlands and foothills, and 2) identify management plans for lands within three large habitat reserves. These conservation plans will set the course by which Orange County plant and wildlife populations survive or die out over the long term. Regardless of whether the NCCP plans succeed in preserving biological diversity, the intrusion of massive toll roads into the heart of at least two of the county's three NCCP reserves will significantly impair human enjoyment of these otherwise tranquil refugia.

A generation ago, American society seemed to more clearly recognize that the quality of human life cannot be separated from the integrity of the surrounding natural environment. Strict laws enacted in the 1970s protecting wetlands and endangered species forestalled destruction and degradation of countless estuaries, lakes, streams, vernal pools, and hillsides of coastal sage scrub. This has permitted achievement of important conservation goals virtually inconceivable two decades ago (see the preceding discussion of recent avian population trends in estuarine and riparian ecosystems). Still, a lack of coherent, responsive land planning mechanisms within most local governmental agencies continues to promote the rapid, large-scale development of natural and agricultural acres into homogenous masses of tract houses, strip malls and business parks. Thus, while the Coastal California Gnatcatcher is likely to remain here indefinitely, many other native plant and animal species are likely to be extirpated from the county in the coming decades. The standard of living has also certainly declined for residents deeply concerned with the widespread loss of Orange County's once-abundant natural beauty.

In deliberating the county's last major land use decisions (the NCCP for Southern Orange County and the Foothill Transportation Corridor), we ask biologists, politicians and other concerned citizens to consider two specific conservation goals: 1) to stabilize all of the county's extant breeding and wintering bird populations through adequate land set-asides, and 2) to expand and actively manage particularly important habitat areas in order to promote re-establishment of bird species that bred here historically. If, as seems likely, these goals cannot be fully achieved here, we hope that other California communities will learn from our experience.

Locality/Institutional Abbreviations

AG	Agricultural fields and rangelands	PCRP	Peters Canyon Regional Park
AOU	American Ornithologists' Union	PP	Pelican Point
AT	Arroyo Trabuco (south of O'Neill Regional Park)	PT	Plano Trabuco
		RC	Rocky Coastline (south of Newport Beach)
BC	Bolsa Chica State Ecological Reserve		
		RM	Ramakrishna Monastery
BJC	Blue Jay Campground and environs	SAM	Santa Ana Mountains
		SARA	Santa Ana River in Anaheim
BR	Bonita Reservoir	SARM	Santa Ana River Mouth
CBC	Christmas Bird Count(s) - Coastal and Inland	SBCM	San Bernardino County Museum
CBRC	California Bird Records Committee	SBNR	Seal Beach National Wildlife Refuge (abbrev. used in graphs)
CC	Coal Canyon	SBNWR	Seal Beach National Wildlife Refuge (abbrev. used in text)
CCSP	Crystal Cove State Park		
CHSP	Chino Hills State Park	SC	Silverado Canyon
CSUF	California State University, Fullerton	SDC	San Diego Creek
		SDNHM	San Diego Natural History Museum
CSULB	California State University, Long Beach		
		SJC	San Juan Creek
DBSP	Doheny Beach State Park	SJH	San Joaquin Hills
ENC	Environmental Nature Center, Newport Harbor High School	SJM	San Joaquin Marsh
		SORP	Santiago Oaks Regional Park
HBP	Huntington Beach Pier	SRAS	Starr Ranch Audubon Sanctuary
HCP	Huntington Central Park	TRNC	Turtle Rock Nature Center
IL	Irvine Lake (Santiago Reservoir)	UCI	University of California, Irvine
IRP	Irvine Regional Park	UCLA	University of California, Los Angeles, Dickey Collection
LACM	Natural History Museum of Los Angeles County		
LL	Laguna Lake (Fullerton)	UNB	Upper Newport Bay
LNB	Lower Newport Bay	UTC	Upper Trabuco Canyon
MRP	William R. Mason Regional Park	VPB	Villa Park Basin (behind Villa Park Dam)
MVZ	Museum of Vertebrate Zoology, University of California, Berkeley	W	Widespread
		WFVZ	Western Foundation of Vertebrate Zoology, Camarillo, California
NP	Newport Pier		
OCNC	Oak Canyon Nature Center	WRP	Whiting Regional Park
ONRP	O'Neill Regional Park	YRP	Yorba Regional Park
OR	Oso Reservoir		

Observer/Contributor/Reference Abbreviations

HB	Hal Baxter	RH	Ronald Hurst
PHB	Peter H. Bloom	COJ	Curtis O. Johnson
JSB	Jeffrey S. Boyd	NKJ	Ned K. Johnson
EAC	Eugene A. Cardiff	SAL	Stephen A. Laymon
JAC	John A. Chubb	JL	Janet Linthicum
CC	Carla Cicero	BWM	Barbara W. Massey
CTC	Charles T. Collins	GM	Guy McCaskie
BED	Brian E. Daniels	SGM	Steven G. Morris
JMD	John M. Davis	TN	Theresa Newkirk
RD	Robert Dolan	KLP	Kaaren L. Perry
JLD	Jon L. Dunn	MAP	Michael A. Patten
RAE	Richard A. Erickson	JEP	James E. Pike
G&D	Garrett and Dunn (see References)	VP	Vanche Plumb
SG	Steven Ganley	EAP	Eleanor A. Pugh
KLG	Kimball L. Garrett	RLP	Richard L. Purvis
VG	Virginia Gochenour	RWR	Robert W. Russell
WDG	Wayne D. Gochenour	BKS	Brad K. Schram
MG	Marilyn Green	CWS	Charles W. Sexton
G&M	Grinnell and Miller (see References)	GS	Gertrude Siptroth
		PFS	Paul F. Springer
RAH	Robert A. Hamilton	JCS	John C. Sterling
SGH	Sandra G. Harvill	RRV	Richard R. Veit
LRH	Loren R. Hays	CMW	Clayton M. White
MTH	Matthew T. Heindel	DRW	Douglas R. Willick
S&H	Sexton and Hunt (see References)	JCW	John C. Wilson
TEH	Trude E. Hurd	RZ	Richard Zembal

Symbols Used in Text

#	Specimen (Followed by Museum and Collection Number)
*	Record Under CBRC Review, or Submittal Expected
ø	Record Not Expected to be Submitted to CBRC

Key to Graphs

Abundance Indicators

 Common: Generally present in proper habitat, often in large numbers.

 **Uncommon to Fairly Common:** Typically encountered in appropriate habitat, usually in small to moderate numbers.

 **Rare and Regular:** Small numbers seen virtually every year.

 Casual to Rare and Irregular: Not recorded annually, but showing a pattern of occurrence during the period indicated; generally supported by at least eight records.

A broken bar connected by a thinner bar describes a status that varies from year to year between the specified abundances.

An unconnected broken bar describes a status that varies between absent and the specified abundance.

Unseasonal or accidental records are indicated by a single dot or two connected dots, depending on the visit's duration. Dates and locations are provided in the annotations.

Habitat Codes

District 1: Ocean and Coast
1a oceanic waters beyond the kelp-line
1b inshore waters; rocky and sandy beaches
1c coastal estuaries; salt and brackish marshes

District 2: Lowlands and Hills (Below ~2,000 Feet)
2a freshwater marshes; lakes and reservoirs; rivers; seasonally wet areas
2b low and middle elevation riparian woodlands
2c oak and walnut woodlands; oak savannah; developed oak landscaping
2d low and middle elevation coastal sage scrub; washes; rocky areas
2e low and middle elevation chaparral
2f grasslands; rangelands; agricultural fields; ruderal and disturbed areas
2g urban and suburban neighborhoods; parks; golf courses; orchards; landfills

District 3: Mountains (~2,000 Feet and Higher)
3a upper riparian woodlands
3b mixed oak/coniferous forest
3c high elevation chaparral; high elevation coastal sage scrub; Tecate Cypress forest; cliffs

Breeding Status Indicators

√ regular and widespread   ? historic (no recent records)
† sporadic and/or localized   Ω unknown/suspected

Site Guide
Found in the rightmost column, this bird-finding feature provides recommendations for viewing a given species in the county, considering factors such as seasonal consistency and site accessibility. In general, sites are not recommended for species that are not regularly found at a single locale. Abbreviations used in the site guide are listed on page 32, and all recommended sites can be found on Map 2 in Appendix B.

Species	Habitat	JAN	FEB	MARCH	APRIL	MAY	JUNE	JULY	AUG	SEPT	OCT	NOV	DEC	BREED	SITE GUIDE
Red-throated Loon	1b														PIERS
	2a														
Pacific Loon	1ab														PIERS
Common Loon	1ab														PIERS
	2a														
Pied-billed Grebe	1c,2a													√	W
Horned Grebe	1bc														BC
	2a														
Red-necked Grebe	1bc														
Eared Grebe	1bc,2a														W
Western Grebe	1bc,2a													†	OR
Clark's Grebe	1bc,2a													†	OR
Short-tailed Albatross	1a					(SEE NOTE)									
Black-footed Albatross	1a														
Northern Fulmar	1a														
Pink-footed Shearwater	1a														PIERS
Flesh-footed Shearwater	1a														
Buller's Shearwater	1a														
Sooty Shearwater	1a														PIERS
Short-tailed Shearwater	1a														
Black-vented Shearwater	1a														PIERS
Wilson's Storm-Petrel	1a														
Fork-tailed Storm-Petrel	1a														
Ashy Storm-Petrel	1a														
Black Storm-Petrel	1a														PIERS
Least Storm-Petrel	1a														
White-tailed Tropicbird	1a														
Red-billed Tropicbird	1a														
Masked Booby	1a														
Blue-footed Booby	1a														
American White Pelican	1bc														BC
	2a														SARA

Species	Habitat	JAN	FEB	MARCH	APRIL	MAY	JUNE	JULY	AUG	SEPT	OCT	NOV	DEC	BREED	SITE GUIDE
Brown Pelican	1ab														W
Double-crested Cormorant	1bc,2a													†	W
Brandt's Cormorant	1ab														RC
Pelagic Cormorant	1ab														RC
Magnificent Frigatebird	1ab														
American Bittern	1c,2a													Ω	SJM
Least Bittern	1c,2a													Ω	SJM
Great Blue Heron	1bc,2a													†	W
Great Egret	1bc,2a													†	W
Snowy Egret	1c,2a													†	W
Little Blue Heron	1c														
Tricolored Heron	1c														
Reddish Egret	1c														
Cattle Egret	1c,2af													?	SJM
Green Heron	1bc,2ab													†	SJM
Black-cr. Night-Heron	1bc,2a													†	DBSP
Yellow-cr. Night-Heron	1c,2a														
White-faced Ibis	1c,2a														SJM
Roseate Spoonbill	1c														
Wood Stork	1c														
Fulvous Whistling-Duck	1c,2a					(SEE NOTE)									
Tundra Swan	1c,2af														
Gr. White-fronted Goose	1c,2a														
Snow Goose	1c,2a														
Ross' Goose	2a														
Emperor Goose	1														
Brant	1a														PIERS
	1bc														BC
Canada Goose															
B.c. moffitti	1c,2af														SJM
B.c. taverneri	1c,2af														SJM
B.c. leucopareia	2a					(SEE NOTE)									
B.c. minima	2a														

Species	Habitat	JAN	FEB	MARCH	APRIL	MAY	JUNE	JULY	AUG	SEPT	OCT	NOV	DEC	BREED	SITE GUIDE
Wood Duck	2a													†	
Green-winged Teal															
A.c. crecca	1c,2a														
A.c. carolinensis	1c,2a														UNB
Mallard	1c,2a													√	SJM
Northern Pintail	1c,2a													†	SJM
Garganey	2a														
Blue-winged Teal	1c,2a													†	BC
Cinnamon Teal	1c,2a													√	SJM
Northern Shoveler	1c,2a														SJM
Gadwall	1c,2a													†	SJM
Eurasian Wigeon	1c,2a														UNB
American Wigeon	1c,2a														UNB
Canvasback	1c,2a														UNB
Redhead	1c,2a													†	SJM
Ring-necked Duck	2a														SJC
Greater Scaup	1bc														BC
Lesser Scaup	1bc,2a														BC
King Eider	1bc														
Harlequin Duck	1bc														
Oldsquaw	1bc														
Black Scoter	1b														PIERS
Surf Scoter	1bc														PIERS
White-winged Scoter	1bc														PIERS
Common Goldeneye	1bc,2a														BC
Barrow's Goldeneye	1c,2a														
Bufflehead	1c,2a														BC
Hooded Merganser	1c,2a														
Common Merganser	2a														SARA
	1c														
Red-breasted Merganser	1bc														BC
	2a														
Ruddy Duck	1c,2a													√	SJM

Species	Habitat	JAN	FEB	MARCH	APRIL	MAY	JUNE	JULY	AUG	SEPT	OCT	NOV	DEC	BREED	SITE GUIDE
Turkey Vulture	1c,2,3	████████████████████████████████████												†	W
California Condor							(SEE NOTE)								
Osprey	1bc,2a				····									Ω	IL
White-tailed Kite	1c,2abcf	■■■■■■■■■■■■■■■■■■■■■■■■■■■■■■■■■■■■■												√	SJM
Mississippi Kite							▬								
Bald Eagle	1c,2a	··		·		(SEE NOTE)						·		Ω	
Northern Harrier	1c,2abcdef	━━━━━━━━━━━━━━━━━━								━━━━━━━━━━━━━━━━━				†	SJM
Sharp-shinned Hawk	2,3	████████████████					··			████████████████					
Cooper's Hawk	2,3	████████████████████████████████████												√	IRP
Red-shouldered Hawk	2bcg	████████████████████████████████████												√	W
Broad-winged Hawk										·		·			
Swainson's Hawk	2	·		····						·:	·				
Zone-tailed Hawk	2,3	····				·			··		····				IRP
Red-tailed Hawk															
B.j. calurus	1c,2	████████████████		████████████████████████										√	W
	3													†	
B.j. harlani	1c,2,3	········		·									·▪		
Ferruginous Hawk	2cf			····						·	▪ ····				
Rough-legged Hawk		▪				(SEE NOTE)					·		▪		
Golden Eagle	2cdef,3													†	IRP
American Kestrel	1c,2,3	████████████████████████████████████												√	W
Merlin															
F.c. columbarius/bendirei	1c,2,3				····					▪··········					BC
F.c. suckleyi	1c,2,3	▪━━━			·							━━▪			
F.c. richardsonii	1c,2,3										·	·			
Peregrine Falcon	1c,2acg													†	BC
Prairie Falcon	1c,2acf,3bc													?	CC
California Quail	2bcdef,3bc	████████████████████████████████████												√	OCNC
Mountain Quail	3c	━━━━━━━━━━━━━━━━━━━━━━━━━━━━━━━━━━━━												√	W
Yellow Rail	1c,2a						(SEE NOTE)								
Black Rail	1c	·		·		(SEE NOTE)									UNB
Clapper Rail	1c	████████████████████████████████████												†	UNB
	2a	···												Ω	SJM

Species	Habitat	JAN	FEB	MARCH	APRIL	MAY	JUNE	JULY	AUG	SEPT	OCT	NOV	DEC	BREED	SITE GUIDE
Virginia Rail	1c,2a													†	UNB
Sora	1c,2a													†	SJM
Common Moorhen	2a													†	UNB
American Coot	1c,2a													√	W
Sandhill Crane	1c,2a														
Black-bellied Plover	1bc														BC
	2af														SARA
American Golden-Plover	1c,2a														
Pacific Golden-Plover	1c,2a														SBNR
Snowy Plover	1bc													†	BC
Semipalmated Plover	1bc														BC
	2a														SJM
Killdeer	1bc,2af													√	W
Mountain Plover	2f					(SEE NOTE)									
American Oystercatcher	1b														
Black Oystercatcher	1b														RC
Black-necked Stilt	1c,2a													√	BC
American Avocet	1c,2a													√	BC
Greater Yellowlegs	1c,2a														BC
Lesser Yellowlegs	1c,2a														BC
Solitary Sandpiper	1c,2a														SJM
Willet	1bc														W
	2a														SARA
Wandering Tattler	1b														RC
Spotted Sandpiper	1bc,2a													†	SJM
Whimbrel	1bc														BC
	2a														SJM
Long-billed Curlew	1bc,2af														BC
Marbled Godwit	1bc														BC
	2af														SJM
Ruddy Turnstone	1bc														BC
Black Turnstone	1b														RC

Species	Habitat	JAN	FEB	MARCH	APRIL	MAY	JUNE	JULY	AUG	SEPT	OCT	NOV	DEC	BREED	SITE GUIDE
Surfbird	1b				▄▄	····		·· ········							RC
Red Knot	1bc	▄▄▄▄▄						▄▄▄▄▄▄					▄▄		BC
Sanderling	1bc	▄▄▄▄▄			▄▄▄▄		▄▄▄		▄▄▄▄▄▄▄▄▄▄▄▄						BC
Semipalmated Sandpiper	1c,2a						·: ···		·· ▪▪						SJM
Western Sandpiper	1bc,2a	▄▄▄▄▄			▄▄▄		▄▄▄▄▄▄▄▄▄▄▄▄								UNB
Little Stint	1c,2a						▪								
Least Sandpiper	1bc,2a	▄▄▄▄▄▄▄			▪	▪	▄▄▄▄▄▄▄								UNB
White-rumped Sandpiper	1c,2a								▪						
Baird's Sandpiper	1c,2a						··· ···		▪ ▪						SJM
Pectoral Sandpiper	1c,2a			▪ ▪				▪ ····	▄▄▄▄▄▄▄▄▄						SJM
Sharp-tailed Sandpiper	1c,2a								▪						
Dunlin	1c	▄▄▄▄▄▄▄			▪	··	▪ ▪:·	▪	····	▄▄▄▄▄▄					BC
	2a	▄▄▄▄▄▄			····				···	▄▄▄▄					SJM
Curlew Sandpiper	1c,2a						▪								
Stilt Sandpiper	1c,2a	▪ ▄▄▄					▪	▪ ··· ▪	▪						
Ruff	1c,2a							···· ▪ ▪							
Short-billed Dowitcher	1c						▄▄▄▄▄▄▄▄▄								UNB
	2a			········	····		▄▄▄▄▄▄▄								SJM
Long-billed Dowitcher	1c,2a	▄▄▄▄▄▄			▪		▄▄▄▄▄▄▄▄								W
Common Snipe	1c,2abf	▄▄▄▄▄▄			▪				▄▄▄▄▄▄						SJM
Wilson's Phalarope	1c,2a				···· ▄▄		▄▄▄▄▄▄		▪ ▪						BC
Red-necked Phalarope	1	▪ ▪		·▪:	▄▄▄▄▄		▄▄▄▄▄▄▄	···· ▪							BC
	2a		▪	·········		······················									SJM
Red Phalarope	1ab	▄···	········	········	▄▄ ▄		▪ ▪ ····		▄▄ ▪ ▄ ▄						PIERS
Pomarine Jaeger	1a	▄▄▄▄▄▄						▄▄▄▄▄▄▄					▄▄		PIERS
Parasitic Jaeger	1ab					▪	·▪:		▄▄▄▄▄▄						PIERS
Long-tailed Jaeger	1						▪	▪ ▪							
South Polar Skua	1a						▪								
Laughing Gull	1		▪			···	▪:· ▪ ····						▪		
Franklin's Gull	1,2a	▪▪				·:·		▪	▪ ············						
Little Gull	1,2a	▪		▪								▄▄			

Species	Habitat	JAN	FEB	MARCH	APRIL	MAY	JUNE	JULY	AUG	SEPT	OCT	NOV	DEC	BREED	SITE GUIDE
Black-headed Gull	1														
Bonaparte's Gull	1,2a														SARM
Heermann's Gull	1														W
Mew Gull	1bc,2ag														SARM
Ring-billed Gull	1bc,2afg														W
California Gull	1,2afg														W
Herring Gull	1,2ag														DBSP
Thayer's Gull	1,2ag														DBSP
Lesser Black-backed Gull	1														
Yellow-footed Gull	1														
Western Gull															
L.o. occidentalis	1,2ag														DBSP
L.o. wymani	1													†	W
	2ag														SARA
Glaucous-winged Gull	1														DBSP
	2ag														
Glaucous Gull	1bc														
Black-legged Kittiwake	1ab														
Sabine's Gull	1a														
Ivory Gull	1														
Gull-billed Tern	1bc														
Caspian Tern	1bc													†	BC
	2a														SARA
Royal Tern	1													†	BC
Elegant Tern	1bc													†	BC
Sandwich Tern	1bc														
Common Tern	1														BC
	2a														
Arctic Tern	1a														
Forster's Tern	1bc													†	BC
	2a														SARA
Least Tern	1bc													†	BC
	2a														SJM

Species	Habitat	JAN	FEB	MARCH	APRIL	MAY	JUNE	JULY	AUG	SEPT	OCT	NOV	DEC	BREED	SITE GUIDE
Sooty Tern	1														
Black Tern	1bc,2a														BC
Black Skimmer	1bc													†	BC
	2a														SJM
Common Murre	1a														
Pigeon Guillemot	1a														
Xantus' Murrelet	1a														
Craveri's Murrelet	1a														
Ancient Murrelet	1a														
Cassin's Auklet	1a														
Rhinoceros Auklet	1a														
Horned Puffin	1ab														
Band-tailed Pigeon	2c,3ab													√	W
White-winged Dove	2fg														
Mourning Dove	2,3													√	W
Common Ground-Dove	2fg													√	HCP
Ruddy Ground-Dove	2fg														
Black-billed Cuckoo	2b														
Yellow-billed Cuckoo	2b	(SEE NOTE)							(SEE NOTE)					Ω	
Greater Roadrunner	2de,3c													√	OCNC
Groove-billed Ani															
Barn Owl	1c,2													√	IRP
	3													†	BJC
Western Screech-Owl	2bcg,3ab													√	IRP
Great Horned Owl	2,3													√	IRP
Burrowing Owl	2f													†	
Spotted Owl	3ab													†	UTC
Long-eared Owl	2bc													†	TRWP
Short-eared Owl	1c,2af													Ω	SJM
Northern Saw-whet Owl	3ab													†	SC
Lesser Nighthawk	2d													†	IRP
	2ag														SJM

Species	Habitat	JAN	FEB	MARCH	APRIL	MAY	JUNE	JULY	AUG	SEPT	OCT	NOV	DEC	BREED	SITE GUIDE
Common Nighthawk															
Common Poorwill	2de,3c													√	W
	2g														
Black Swift	2,3														
Chimney Swift	2,3														
Vaux's Swift	2,3														W
White-throated Swift	2,3													√	SORP
Broad-billed Hummingbird	2bg														
Bl.-chin. Hummingbird	2bcdeg,3a													√	HCP
Anna's Hummingbird	2bcdeg,3													√	W
Costa's Hummingbird	2bdeg,3c													√	SORP
Calliope Hummingbird	2,3ac														SAM
Rufous Hummingbird	2bdeg,3														OCNC
Allen's Hummingbird															
S.s. sasin	2bcdeg,3														W
S.s. sedentarius	2bg													√	HCP
Belted Kingfisher	1c,2a													†	VPB
Lewis' Woodpecker	2bc														
Acorn Woodpecker	2bc,3b													√	IRP
	2g														
Yellow-bellied Sapsucker	2bcg														
Red-naped Sapsucker	2bcg														
Red-breasted Sapsucker	2bcg,3ab														HCP
Williamson's Sapsucker	2g,3ab														
Nuttall's Woodpecker	2bc,3ab													√	IRP
Downy Woodpecker	2bg													√	BR
Hairy Woodpecker	3ab													†	UTC
White-headed Woodpecker	3b														
Northern Flicker															
Yellow-shafted forms	2bcg														
Red-shafted forms	2bcg,3													√	IRP
Olive-sided Flycatcher	2bcg,3a														HCP
	3b													†	UTC

Species	Habitat	JAN	FEB	MARCH	APRIL	MAY	JUNE	JULY	AUG	SEPT	OCT	NOV	DEC	BREED	SITE GUIDE
Greater Pewee	2bcg														
Western Wood-Pewee	2bcg													†	SRAS
	3ab													√	UTC
Willow Flycatcher	2bg,3a													Ω	HCP
Least Flycatcher	2bg														
Hammond's Flycatcher	2bcg														HCP
Dusky Flycatcher	2bg														
Gray Flycatcher	2bg														
Pacific-slope Flycatcher	2bcg													†	SORP
	3a													√	UTC
Black Phoebe	1c,2abg,3a													√	W
Eastern Phoebe	2bg														
Say's Phoebe	2cdfg													†	W
Vermilion Flycatcher	2abfg														
Dusky-capped Flycatcher	2														
Ash-throated Flycatcher	2,3													√	OCNC
Great Crested Flycatcher	2														
Brown-crested Flycatcher	2														
Sulphur-bellied Flycatcher	2														
Tropical Kingbird	2ag														
Cassin's Kingbird	2													√	SJM
Thick-billed Kingbird	2														
Western Kingbird	2													†	SORP
Eastern Kingbird	2														
Scissor-tailed Flycatcher	2														
Horned Lark	2f													†	AG
Purple Martin	2abc,3b													†	
Tree Swallow	1c,2ab													†	SJM
Violet-green Swallow	2abcdef,3													†	SC
N. Rough-winged Swall.	1c,2abg													√	SJM

Species	Habitat	JAN	FEB	MARCH	APRIL	MAY	JUNE	JULY	AUG	SEPT	OCT	NOV	DEC	BREED	SITE GUIDE
Bank Swallow	1c,2ab													Ω	SJM
Cliff Swallow	1c,2,3													√	W
Barn Swallow	1c,2													√	W
Steller's Jay															
Western Scrub-Jay	2bcdeg,3bc													√	W
Clark's Nutcracker															
American Crow	1c,2													√	W
Common Raven	2,3													√	W
Mountain Chickadee	3b													†	UTC
	2g														
Plain Titmouse OAK	2bc,3													√	SORP
Bushtit	2abcdeg,3a													√	W
Red-breasted Nuthatch	2g,3b														
White-breasted Nuthatch	2c,3ab													√	IRP
Pygmy Nuthatch	2g,3b														
Brown Creeper	2bcg,3ab														
Cactus Wren	2d													√	WRP
Rock Wren	2d,3c													†	CHSP
Canyon Wren	2d,3ac													†	SJH
Bewick's Wren	2bcdeg,3ac													√	W
House Wren	2b													√	SJH
	2cdeg													†	HCP
	3ab													√	W
Winter Wren	2bcg,3a														
Sedge Wren	2a														
Marsh Wren	1c,2a													√	UNB
American Dipper	3a														
Golden-crowned Kinglet	2bcg														
	3ab														
Ruby-crowned Kinglet	2bcg,3ab														W
Blue-gray Gnatcatcher	2abcdeg													†	HCP
	3c													√	BJC

Species	Habitat	JAN	FEB	MARCH	APRIL	MAY	JUNE	JULY	AUG	SEPT	OCT	NOV	DEC	BREED	SITE GUIDE
California Gnatcatcher	2d													√	CCSP
	2bf													†	
Western Bluebird	2bcfg,3													†	YRP
Mountain Bluebird	2f														
Townsend's Solitaire	3														
Swainson's Thrush	2bg,3a													†	PCRP
Hermit Thrush	2bceg,3					(SEE NOTE)								Ω	HCP
Rufous-backed Robin	2g														
American Robin	2bceg,3a													†	HCP
Varied Thrush	2bceg,3														BJC
Wrentit	2deg,3c													√	W
Gray Catbird	2bg														
Northern Mockingbird	2bcdeg													√	W
Sage Thrasher	2dfg														
Brown Thrasher	2bg														
Bendire's Thrasher	2														
California Thrasher	2bcde													√	CCSP
	3ac													√	W
Yellow Wagtail	2a														
Black-backed Wagtail	2a														
Red-throated Pipit	2f														
American Pipit	2afg														AG
Sprague's Pipit	2f														
Bohemian Waxwing	2,3														
Cedar Waxwing	2bceg,3ac													Ω	HCP
Phainopepla	2bcdeg,3													√	IRP
Loggerhead Shrike	2cfg													√	SJM
White-eyed Vireo	2bg														
Bell's Vireo															
V.b. bellii/medius	2b														
V.b. pusillus	2b													†	MRP

Species	Habitat	JAN	FEB	MARCH	APRIL	MAY	JUNE	JULY	AUG	SEPT	OCT	NOV	DEC	BREED	SITE GUIDE
Solitary Vireo															
V.s. solitarius	2bcg														
V.s. plumbeus	2bcg														HCP
	3ab														
V.s. cassinii	2bcg														HCP
	3ab													?	
Yellow-throated Vireo	2bcg														
Hutton's Vireo	2bc,3ab													√	IRP
	2g													†	HCP
Warbling Vireo	2bcg													†	SRAS
	3a													†	UTC
Philadelphia Vireo	2bg														
Red-eyed Vireo	2bg														
Yellow-green Vireo	2bg														
Blue-winged Warbler	2bg														
Golden-winged Warbler	2bcg														
Tennessee Warbler	2bcg														
Orange-cr. Warbler	2bcdeg,3													√	W
Nashville Warbler	2bcg														HCP
	3ab														
Virginia's Warbler	2bg														
Lucy's Warbler	2bg														
Northern Parula	2bcg														
Yellow Warbler	2bcg													†	SJC
	3a													†	UTC
Chestnut-sided Warbler	2bg														
Magnolia Warbler	2bg														
Cape May Warbler	2bg														
Black-throated Blue Warbler	2bg														
Yellow-rumped Warbler															
"Myrtle"	2bcg,3														HCP
"Audubon's"	2,3														W
Black-thr. Gray Warbler	2bcg														HCP
	3b													?	UTC

Species	Habitat	JAN	FEB	MARCH	APRIL	MAY	JUNE	JULY	AUG	SEPT	OCT	NOV	DEC	BREED	SITE GUIDE
Townsend's Warbler	2bcg,3ab														HCP
Hermit Warbler	2bcg,3ab														HCP
Black-thr. Green Warbler	2bg														
Blackburnian Warbler	2bg														
Grace's Warbler	2g														
Pine Warbler	2g														
Prairie Warbler	2bg														
Palm Warbler	2bg														
Bay-breasted Warbler	2bg														
Blackpoll Warbler	2bg														
Cerulean Warbler	2bg														
Black-and-white Warbler	2bg														
American Redstart	2bg														
Prothonotary Warbler	2bg														
Worm-eating Warbler	2bg														
Ovenbird	2bg														
Northern Waterthrush	2bg														
Louisiana Waterthrush	2bg														
Kentucky Warbler	2bg														
Mourning Warbler	2bg														
MacGillivray's Warbler	2bceg,3														HCP
Common Yellowthroat	1c,2abg,3a													√	W
Hooded Warbler	2bg														
Wilson's Warbler	2bcdeg,3														W
Canada Warbler	2bg														
Painted Redstart	2g														
Yellow-breasted Chat	2b													†	BR
Hepatic Tanager	2g														
Summer Tanager	2bg														HCP
Scarlet Tanager	2bg														
Western Tanager	2bcg														HCP
	3ab													†	UTC

Species	Habitat	JAN	FEB	MARCH	APRIL	MAY	JUNE	JULY	AUG	SEPT	OCT	NOV	DEC	BREED	SITE GUIDE
Rose-breasted Grosbeak	2bcg														HCP
Black-headed Grosbeak	2bceg													√	MRP
	3a													√	UTC
Blue Grosbeak	2bf													√	MRP
Lazuli Bunting	2bcdeg,3c													√	HCP
Indigo Bunting	2bg														HCP
Painted Bunting	2bg														
Dickcissel	2bfg														
Green-tailed Towhee	2,3														
Spotted Towhee	2bcdeg,3													√	W
California Towhee	2,3c													√	W
Cassin's Sparrow															
Rufous-crowned Sparrow	2de,3c													√	CHSP
American Tree Sparrow	2fg														
Chipping Sparrow	2bcfg														IRP
	3													†	BJC
Clay-colored Sparrow	2bfg														
Brewer's Sparrow	2bfg														
Field Sparrow	2fg														
Black-chinned Sparrow	2de,3c													√	W
Vesper Sparrow	2cdfg														
Lark Sparrow	2cdfg													√	IRP
Black-throated Sparrow	2														
Sage Sparrow	2de,3c													†	CC
Lark Bunting	2fg														
Savannah Sparrow northern/interior ssp.	1c,2cfg														W
P.s. beldingi	1c													√	BC
P.s. rostratus	1c														SBNR
Grasshopper Sparrow	2f													√	SJH
Le Conte's Sparrow	1c,2afg														
Nelson's Sharp-tailed Sparrow	1c														UNB

Species	Habitat	JAN	FEB	MARCH	APRIL	MAY	JUNE	JULY	AUG	SEPT	OCT	NOV	DEC	BREED	SITE GUIDE
Fox Sparrow															
iliaca group	2														
unalaschcensis grp.	2bdeg,3ac														SAM
schistacea group	2de,3ac														SAM
megarhynchus group	3ac														SAM
Song Sparrow	1c,2abg													√	W
	3a													√	SC
Lincoln's Sparrow	1c,2abg														SJM
Swamp Sparrow	1c,2ab														UNB
White-throated Sparrow	2bge														
Golden-cr. Sparrow	2bcdeg,3														IRP
White-crowned Sparrow															
Z.l. gambelii	2,3														W
Z.l. oriantha	2														
Z.l. pugetensis	2														HCP
Harris' Sparrow	2														
Dark-eyed Junco															
"Slate-colored"	2bcdeg,3														IRP
"Oregon"	2bdeg													†	IRP
	2c,3													√	W
"Pink-sided"	2bcdeg														
"Gray-headed"	2bcdeg														IRP
McCown's Longspur	2f														
Lapland Longspur	2f														
Chestnut-collared Longspur	2f														
Bobolink	2abgf														
Red-winged Blackbird	1c,2abfg													√	W
Tricolored Blackbird	2abfg													†	
Western Meadowlark	2cf													√	AG
Yellow-headed Blackbird	1c,2af													†	SJM
Rusty Blackbird	1c,2a														
Brewer's Blackbird	1c,2acfg													√	W
Great-tailed Grackle	1c,2ag													†	
Brown-headed Cowbird	2fg													√	W
	2abcde,3													√	W

Species	Habitat	JAN	FEB	MARCH	APRIL	MAY	JUNE	JULY	AUG	SEPT	OCT	NOV	DEC	BREED	SITE GUIDE
Orchard Oriole	2bg														
Hooded Oriole	2bg													√	W
Baltimore Oriole	2g														
Bullock's Oriole	2bc,3a													√	OCNC
	2g													√	HCP
Scott's Oriole	2bcdeg														
Purple Finch	2bceg													?	ONRP
	3													†	UTC
House Finch	1bc,2,3													√	W
Red Crossbill	2g,3b														
Pine Siskin	2bcg,3														IRP
Lesser Goldfinch	2,3													√	W
Lawrence's Goldfinch	2,3													†	CHSP
American Goldfinch	2abcg,3													√	PCRP

Annotations

Red-throated Loon: One at Mile Square Park 10 May 1983 was late for an inland bird.

Pacific Loon: Fairly common winter visitor to nearshore waters, with a high daily count of at least 50 off Corona del Mar 23 December 1982 (DRW); approximately 75 flying north off NP 5 May 1995 was a high daily count during migration. Four inland records: SJM "February-March" 1973; OCNC 27 November 1984-15 March 1985; SARA 1 March 1988; and SARA 23-31 October 1993.

Common Loon: One unseasonal inland record: SARA 19 July-9 August 1980.

Pied-billed Grebe: Fairly common resident of tule-bordered ponds and reservoirs throughout the lowlands and foothills. Numbers are augmented in fall and winter, when the birds occupy a wider range of habitats along the coast.

Horned Grebe: Uncommon along the coast. A weak spring passage is evident during March and April. Two late spring records: BC 23 April-10 July 1985, and HCP 25 April-2 May 1992 (inland). An early fall migrant was at UNB 28 September 1991.

Red-necked Grebe: Four acceptable records: BC 24 April 1982 (late); LNB 13 February-3 March 1984; LNB 26 January 1985; and LNB 25 December 1995. S&H (1979) published four coastal CBC records (1953, 1959, 1962, and 1969) and six non-CBC records between November and February (1948, 1953, three in 1963, 1964). Due to lack of documentation, and this species' extreme rarity this far south, we consider these records unacceptable.

Eared Grebe: Individuals and small groups summer at scattered locations from the coast to the foothills, but evidence of nesting is lacking. A count of 103 at Sand Canyon Reservoir 28 November 1994 (RAH) was notable for a small reservoir.

Western Grebe: Abundant winter visitor to nearshore waters, with a representative high count of approximately 1100 off Huntington Beach 23 February 1995 (JEP). Generally common in winter and rare in summer at larger inland reservoirs, nesting at Oso Reservoir when conditions are appropriate there. Gallagher (1993) reported a pair of *Aechmophorus* grebes with one chick at this reservoir in "May 1988," and fishermen reported seeing family groups in 1993 and 1994. In 1995, approximately 100 pairs of Western Grebes summered there, many nesting (chicks first observed 15 June). At least two mixed pairs of Western and Clark's (or hybrids) were present, as were small numbers of apparent hybrid adults.

Clark's Grebe: Along the coast and at larger inland reservoirs, Clark's Grebe is generally uncommon from early October through mid-April and rare the rest of the year. Moderate numbers nest at Oso Reservoir when conditions are appropriate there. Gallagher (1993) reported a pair of *Aechmophorus* grebes with one chick at this reservoir in "May 1988," and fishermen reported seeing family groups in 1993 and 1994. In 1995, approximately 50 pairs of Clark's Grebes summered there, many nesting (chicks first observed 15 June).

Short-tailed Albatross: This was a regular visitant offshore and along the coast until the late 19th Century. A specimen taken from Newport in 1898 (Grinnell 1898) represents the last county record.

Black-footed Albatross: One was observed at Lausen Knoll 30 May 1989.

Northern Fulmar: This irruptive seabird is irregularly visible from shore. Most records are of light morph birds. Adequate observer coverage well offshore would likely reveal it to be fairly common during some years and absent to scarce during others. Two unseasonal nearshore records: Seal Beach Pier (sick) 17 July 1991, and a "freshly dead" bird washed up on Huntington Beach 29 August 1993. One onshore record: BC 10 November 1984.

Pink-footed Shearwater: Graph represents the expected status if offshore waters were adequately covered. RRV (in litt.) reports a significant regional increase since 1989. Small numbers have been observed from shore from June through August; daily counts of ten to 20 are exceptional. At least 100 observed off Newport Beach 21 July 1992 (during a period of unusually warm water) was a high count.

Flesh-footed Shearwater: One was observed in a large concentration of seabirds one to two miles off CCSP 29 December 1995.

Buller's Shearwater: Two acceptable records of fall migrants: one off Dana Point 5 September 1992, and one off PP 16 October 1994. G&D (1981) attributed three "off San Clemente" 2 November 1957 to Orange County, but the birds were "more than 55 miles from the mainland" near San Clemente Island (*Audubon Field Notes* 12:58).

Sooty Shearwater: Regularly visible from shore in summer and fall, with typical daily counts in the range of ten to 200. RRV (in litt.) reports a significant decrease since 1987. Small numbers are usually present during winter, a period when confusion with Short-tailed Shearwater poses difficulties.

Short-tailed Shearwater: Rare, possibly regular winter visitor to county waters; determining the true status is difficult due to confusion with the similar Sooty Shearwater. One that washed up on Huntington Beach 11 March 1976 is preserved as a skeleton (#CSULB 5258).

Black-vented Shearwater: Readily seen from shore in numbers that vary markedly from year to year. During "peak" years, 200 to 1000 or more may be viewed in a day during late fall/winter; as few as 20 are seen per day during "off" years.

Summer records were few before 1992, when elevated oceanic water temperatures brought an unprecedented influx of this and other oceanic species to the county's nearshore waters. The top estimated daily count during this period was 30,000 on 31 July at NP. This phenomenon was apparently unique for recent times, as only small numbers have been observed during subsequent summers; the graph depicts the typical range of variability.

Wilson's Storm-Petrel: One was observed four miles off Huntington Beach 30 July 1990.

Fork-tailed Storm-Petrel: Very rare, irregular visitant, recorded in spring and late fall. Spring records include the following: Wyman (1917) reported a series of nine birds washed up on Sunset Beach 15 May-1 June 1916 (#LACM 1322, 1323, 1338, 1339, 86404); eight off NP 21 April 1995; two or three off Laguna Beach 21 April 1995; and one to three off NP 5-6 May 1995. One observed off PP 25 October 1992 was somewhat early for fall/winter.

Ashy Storm-Petrel: During some years, small numbers are seen from shore May through August (maximum of about ten per day). Otherwise, the graph depicts the expected status well offshore.

Black Storm-Petrel: Normally the storm-petrel most readily viewed from shore. When visible, typical daily counts from shore range from two to ten, with high counts of 100 or more.

Least Storm-Petrel: Seldom visible from shore; the graph represents the expected status well offshore. Three early records between April and June: off NP 17 June 1992; off PP 27 June 1993; and an extremely early bird off NP 21 April 1995. This storm-petrel was readily seen from shore for about two weeks in late July 1992 during an unprecedented nearshore influx that was tied to warm water conditions; the high count was 80 off Newport Beach 21 July 1992.

White-tailed Tropicbird: A widely observed adult present regularly at UNB 24 May-23 June 1964 was the first record for the west coast of North America. For a complete account, see Hetrick and McCaskie (1965).

Red-billed Tropicbird: One was off San Juan Capistrano 15 June 1952, and one was "near Avalon" 9 July 1974.

Masked Booby: A sub-adult was observed off NP 30 June 1992.

Blue-footed Booby: A sub-adult female found sick at a Huntington Beach school 7 September 1990 died in captivity 12 September 1990 (*; #LACM 109238). van Rossem (1922a) speculated that a booby off Sunset Beach 25 October 1921 may have been this species.

American White Pelican: S&H (1979) called this pelican "uncommon (sparse and irregular) along coast and in bays...fall, winter and spring. Rarely seen inland..." Since 1988/89, flocks of 100 or more have been present along the upper Santa Ana River in fall and/or winter, with a high count of approximately 600 during January 1993. A wing-tagged bird present in this flock during winter 1992/93 was traced to a breeding colony in British Columbia. Individuals and small flocks (typically containing fewer than 30 birds) are rare to uncommon elsewhere, with most records from BC, UNB and SJM during fall and winter.

Brown Pelican: The status of this familiar coastal bird drops to "fairly common" during the breeding season, when many Brown Pelicans head south (presumably) to breed. Six inland records: four on the inland CBC 29 December 1948; SARA 15 September-8 October 1982; Mission Viejo 28 March 1985 (#WFVZ 32951); SARA 2-23 January 1993, with two present on 16 January (considered two records); and SARA 4 September 1993.

Double-crested Cormorant: Non-breeding birds are fairly common along the coast and at SARA during summer. A small breeding colony containing up to 40 pairs has been established at the south end of Anaheim Lake since at least 1988 (Gallagher 1993). This cormorant has nested at Santa Ana River Lakes in recent years, but RAH observed no active nests there in 1995.

Brandt's Cormorant: While numbers seen from shore vary widely from day to day, this cormorant is best described as a fairly common spring migrant, March through early May, and an uncommon winter visitor. It is locally fairly common along the rocky coastline south of Newport Beach. Brandt's Cormorant typically outnumbers Pelagic, although roughly equal numbers may be encountered south of Newport Beach on rare days.

Pelagic Cormorant: Uncommon during migration and winter, occurring primarily along the coast from Corona del Mar south, where numbers rarely match those of Brandt's Cormorant. Recorded twice away from the open ocean: BC 9 September 1983, and SARM 16-17 October 1993.

Magnificent Frigatebird: Records, most pertaining to immatures, average one or two per year; a total count of seven in 1988 (including four at Balboa Pier 28 June 1988) was unusual. Identification must be made with care at all seasons, since some plumages are nearly indistinguishable from the Great Frigatebird (*Fregata minor*), which has occurred in California. Two unseasonal reports of frigatebirds at BC were likely Magnificents, but are left unidentified to species since some diagnostic marks were not observed: 19 January 1985 (immature on the ground), and 19 February 1993 (adult female flying over).

American Bittern: S&H (1979) considered this species "fairly common at SJM...uncommon in salt marshes in fall and winter." American Bitterns are now uncommon during winter at SJM, UNB, and probably SBNWR; they are rare in marshy habitats elsewhere. Willett (1933) reported nesting at Sunset Beach 3 May 1917. Recent indications of possible nesting at SJM include: two "pumping" on 18 April 1991 with one seen 26 May 1991, and "at least a few" calling during summer 1994. One at least five or six miles off Newport Beach 23 September 1995 was unexpected.

Least Bittern: Adults, usually single birds, are rarely found in suitable habitat (dense tules, cat-tails, etc. in freshwater and brackish marshes) during the nesting season. Young birds were found at SJM in summer 1979 (GS pers. comm.). One in coastal salt marsh along the boardwalk at BC 23 October 1985 was unexpected.

Great Blue Heron: Non-breeding birds are uncommon to fairly common in summer. Moderate numbers nest at Anaheim Lake (up to 50 pairs), Irvine Lake (up to 40 pairs), Santa Ana River Lakes (up to 18 pairs), and SBNWR (up to 12 pairs); scattered colonies of five or fewer pairs exist elsewhere.

Great Egret: Non-breeding birds are generally uncommon in summer, locally fairly common at SARA. An active nest at Irvine Lake in 1992 provided the county's first confirmed nesting record (Gallagher 1993). Nest-building was observed at both Anaheim Lake and the Santa Ana River Lakes in 1990. Gallagher (1993) reported at least 20 active nests with young at the Santa Ana River Lakes in 1993; similar numbers continue to summer there, presumably nesting (the area is not closely monitored).

Snowy Egret: Non-breeding birds are generally uncommon in summer, locally fairly common at SARA. Nesting was first confirmed in 1990, when 15 active nests were observed at the Santa Ana River Lakes; at least 20 pairs nested there in 1993 (Gallagher 1993). Similar numbers continue to summer there, presumably nesting (the area is not closely monitored). An apparent Snowy Egret X Little Blue Heron hybrid was at DBSP 7 October 1990.

Little Blue Heron: At least ten fall/winter records. The earliest fall arrival was an immature at BC 17 August-13 September 1986. An immature lingered at UNB (molting into adult plumage) 28 January-12 August 1990. One record of a spring migrant: Seal Beach 11 May 1986 (adult). An adult at SJM 8-31 July 1984 was unseasonal.

Tricolored Heron: Only records from 1990 and later are under CBRC review. The county's first record, UNB 22 March-15 May 1967, was unseasonal. Reports from BC 25 May and 10 June 1981 are considered a single late spring record. Two midsummer records: BC 4 July 1985, and UNB 19-27 June to BC 2-3 July 1994 (*; considered one record). At least 13 fall/winter records, one of which is under CBRC review. An early migrant was at BC 27 August 1972. Five at Seal Beach in fall/winter 1972/73 was an extraordinary concentration.

Reddish Egret: Four records of spring migrants, all since 1992: SBNWR 12 April-9 May 1992; BC 29 April-31 May 1994 (*); SBNWR 24-30 April 1994 (*); and SBNWR 21 May 1995 (*). One unusual summer record: UNB 31 July 1970. Three records of fall migrants, two of these inland: BC 6-13 October 1963; SARA 10 September 1984; and SARA 10-28 October 1995 (*). Three winter records: UNB 16 November 1961 to "May" 1962; BC/SBNWR 8 November-28 February 1981; and BC/SBNWR 18 October 1992-20 March 1993. S&H (1979) published one at BC 11 November 1967, but this record was not submitted for CBRC review and details of the sighting are unknown.

Cattle Egret: One was recorded 27 December 1962 on the coastal CBC, prior to the state's first well documented record of two in San Diego County 7 March 1964 (McCaskie 1965). Records increased steadily from the early to mid-1980s, when it was an uncommon to fairly common migrant and winter visitor; 58 at SJM 28 December 1984 was a high count. Cattle Egrets have generally been rare since the late 1980s, with a modest fall/winter influx in 1992/93. Gallagher (1993) reported "a small number...with young" at Laguna Niguel Regional Park in "1987 or 1988." We consider this report too vague to confirm nesting. S&H (1979) reported release of 20 from Lion Country Safari in 1970.

Green Heron: This heron nests uncommonly throughout the lowlands and foothills, using freshwater marshes, reservoirs with vegetated borders, and perennial streams. Green Herons are more widespread and somewhat more common during fall and winter.

Black-crowned Night-Heron: Nesting colonies containing up to approximately 50 pairs are known from DBSP and SARA; Gallagher (1993) reported smaller colonies at other scattered locales near water, primarily in mature eucalyptus. There is evidence of a decline at BC (LRH).

Yellow-crowned Night-Heron: An adult was at SJM 11-14 May 1977 (*Western Tanager* 43[9]:6, S&H 1979). In describing this unusual find, Hoechlin (1978) gave the record as 11 May 1977 only. S&H (1979) listed as hypothetical a sight record from UNB in "August, 1972" (HB).

White-faced Ibis: Referring to southern California as a whole, G&D (1981) considered this ibis "formerly more common in all areas at all seasons." S&H (1979) called it a "rare migrant and winter visitor." This is still the general status in Orange County, although in recent years small to moderate numbers have occurred throughout the year at SJM and lower SDC (occasionally to UNB), with high summer/early fall counts of 29 in 1993, 13 in 1994, and 28 in 1995 (TEH).

Roseate Spoonbill: One post-breeding record: three immatures at SJM 26 June-14 September 1977 (*Western Tanager* 44[3]:6) with two still present 4 October 1977 (*American Birds* 32:256). S&H (1979) did not specify the number of birds involved in this record and their end date, 1 November 1977, is inconsistent with other published accounts, including the one they cited. The CBRC did not review records of this species in 1977.

Wood Stork: Although specific records are lacking, this was probably a regular post-breeding visitant historically (cf. Willett 1933, G&M 1944). Four acceptable records in the past 60 years: UNB 7-25 August 1934; UNB 10 August-5 October 1936; two at Laguna Lakes 20 August 1955; and UNB 8-9 September 1971 (five the first day, three the second day).

Fulvous Whistling-Duck: During the first half of the century, this whistling-duck was considered a locally common summer resident and generally rare migrant in southern and central California, with active or historic breeding stations south to San Diego County (G&M 1944); specific nesting records from Orange County are, however, lacking. One historic winter record: BC 31 January 1900 (#MVZ 31664). S&H (1979) called this an "occasional summer and fall visitor to SJM," and reported free-flying stock at Lion Country Safari. Since the species is widely kept in private collections, recent records (i.e., three at SJM 2 April 1978, two at SARA 11 November 1985) are subject to questions of natural occurrence.

Tundra Swan: Willett (1933) characterized this swan as a "regular visitant in small numbers...south to San Diego County. Much rarer than formerly." Ten records since 1948, four since 1980. As many as 20 commuting between Sand Canyon Reservoir and nearby agricultural fields 19 January-27 February 1982 was a noteworthy concentration.

Greater White-fronted Goose: Willett (1933) called this a "formerly common winter visitant to lowland regions, now met with only occasionally." It now occurs almost annually, with most records pertaining to migrants that do not winter locally. High counts include 34 over HCP 15 October 1984 and 21 at SJM 7 January 1990. Late birds were at Irvine 30 March 1988 and Laguna Reservoir 7 April 1995.

Snow Goose: Grinnell (1898) considered this a "common winter visitant in the lowlands" of the Los Angeles basin (including the Orange County coastal plain). Grinnell et al. (1918) and Willett (1933) described, respectively, vast statewide and regional declines resulting mostly from habitat alteration, market hunting, and crop defense by farmers. G&D (1981) suggested, however, that the coastal decline probably resulted from a "shift in winter range (to the Salton Sea?) rather than an overall decline in the population."

Fewer than five now occur in a typical year, and the species is occasionally missed altogether. Snow Geese seldom arrive before late October; the earliest was one at UNB 6 October 1955. One wintering bird lingered at HCP with a flock of domestic geese until 18 May 1986. Two records of unseasonal individuals at UNB: "summer" 1969 (not graphed), and 5 July 1986-17 May 1987.

Ross' Goose: According to Daggett (1901) this goose was "not often seen" in southern California, but Willett (1912) considered it "fairly common in winter near Santa Ana." Twelve records since 1982, including two late records: YRP 8 March-14 May 1987, and Craig Regional Park "February through early May" 1992. Seven at SARA 7 December 1990-1 January 1991 was a high count.

Emperor Goose: Two records during the same "flight year": Laguna Beach 15 December 1968; and five at Seal Beach 15 December 1968, two of which were shot in late December, with one remaining to 8 March 1969.

Brant: Historically, this goose was abundant along the coast of southern California; Daugherty (1941a) reported "several hundred" at BC in February 1941. The current status (see graph) is similar to that described by S&H (1979). Two recent records of modest northbound flocks: 70 off NP 18 February 1990, and over 200 off NP 9 January 1993 (early). Brant are less likely to be detected during their late fall passage, which takes place well offshore; a southbound flock of 75 several miles off Newport Beach 4 December 1993 was notable. Four inland records from SARA: 22 April 1985; 15 May 1988; and 13 April 1989; and 11 March 1995.

Canada Goose: Flocks of up to several hundred "Western" Canada Geese (*B.c. moffitti*) regularly winter at SBNWR, SJM and Sand Canyon Reservoir, with substantial flocks often wintering elsewhere. At Sand Canyon Reservoir/Quail Hill, Butler (1990) reported counts of 2500 in 1986, 4150 in 1988, and 1350 in 1989; numbers there have been greatly reduced in subsequent years, although some birds have apparently shifted to SJM. Butler (p. 56) postulated a local decline resulting "possibly from habitat loss here or from changing conditions along migration routes." Two early records of *moffitti*: six at SJM 29 September 1992, and 12 flying over Irvine 13 September 1993.

Birds belonging to smaller races are often found in larger flocks of "Western" Canada Geese; identification of these races requires scrutiny of several characteristics (see Springer and McNab 1990, Springer 1990). "Taverner's" (*B.c. taverneri*) is a rare, regular fall migrant and winter visitor; the similar "Lesser" (*B.c. parvipes*) may also occur. "Cackling" (*B.c. minima*) is of almost annual occurrence. The only definite record of the federally threatened "Aleutian" (*B.c. leucopareia*) is a photograph of at least 50 shot at Santiago Canyon in 1901 (First American Title Insurance, Santa Ana).

Releases of Canada Geese statewide bring an element of uncertainty to determining their status (PFS pers. comm.); for example, a pair of *moffitti* with three young on SDC 2 June 1989 (RAH) almost certainly originated from captive stock.

Wood Duck: Wild birds occur primarily between mid-September and late March; releases are increasingly common, making the "true" status difficult to determine. At least 30 birds, some banded, currently reside at Laguna Lake in Fullerton, and have nested in boxes there each year since 1990 (Gallagher 1993). Wild birds are unrecorded at SJM, where eight banded birds appeared in late summer 1995. In 1988, a large-scale program of introductions and nest box installation commenced in the Prado Basin, Riverside County (Gallagher 1993); an exceptional total of 12 at YRP in "early November" 1993 may have originated from this program.

Green-winged Teal: A late bird was at BC 1 June 1995. Six records of the "Eurasian" race *A.c. crecca*: UNB 19 January-8 February 1969; SJM 26 November 1972; HCP 31 January-28 February 1984; HCP 17 November 1985-18 January 1986; VPB 8 January 1989; and SJM "late January" (RAH) to 5 March 1994. Two records of apparent *crecca* X *carolinensis* intergrades: HCP 18 September-20 November 1984, and SJM 5 March 1994.

Mallard: Wild birds nest sparingly at wetlands of varying quality throughout the lowlands and foothills, and fairly commonly at extensive wetlands such as SJM and SARA. Mallards commonly hybridize with introduced ducks and geese.

Northern Pintail: Historic nesting records from BC (e.g., G&M 1944), with three recent nesting records from there: one pair in 1981; two family groups 28 June 1993; and one family group 1 June 1995.

Garganey: An adult male was at SJM 12-20 September 1990.

Blue-winged Teal: Graph reflects status at BC and UNB, where 10-30 are typically present in fall/winter; 70 at UNB 3 November 1990 was a high count. The species is rare elsewhere, seen most frequently near the coast (e.g., SJM) and along the Santa Ana River. Four family groups at BC on

28 June 1993 provided the first nesting record; a pair with young was observed there 1 June 1995. Three records of apparent Blue-winged X Cinnamon teal hybrids: Laguna Beach 4 January-17 March 1980; SARM 1 December 1984-20 January 1985; and SBNWR 1 January 1992.

Cinnamon Teal: Uncommon summer resident, nesting at scattered freshwater marshes, ponds, and reservoirs with vegetated borders in the lowlands and foothills. This teal is a common migrant and fairly common winter visitor at brackish coastal estuaries and freshwater ponds.

Northern Shoveler: Two records of summer stragglers: SJM 11 June 1990, and five at SJM 6 June 1993 with one remaining to 1 July 1993.

Gadwall: This duck is presently a rare to uncommon breeder at freshwater marshes and vegetated reservoirs; it is locally fairly common to common at BC. It is a fairly common migrant and winter visitor from the coast to the foothills. Until recent years, non-breeders were rare and irregular May to September. Small numbers first nested at SJM and BC in 1993 and 1994, and an estimated 120 were observed at BC 1 June 1995, many in pairs and some with chicks. The local increase may be part of a major status change on both Pacific and Atlantic coasts suggested by Lehman (1994).

Eurasian Wigeon: An irregular visitant before 1986/87, two to eight males have been recorded each fall/winter since then (females are very rarely detected); during this period typical arrival dates have shifted from mid-November to mid-October. Three records of early arrivals: UNB 21 September 1991; UNB 25 September 1992; and SJM 18 September 1993. One in Brea until 9 April 1992 was late.

Two records of apparent Eurasian X American wigeon hybrids: Westminster 1 November 1995, and Lake Forest 21 November 1995. Close examination of both Eurasian and American wigeon may show that hybrids between these species occur regularly (cf. Hamilton 1996).

American Wigeon: Four midsummer records: SARM 3 July 1984; BC 4 July 1984; SJM 25 June-27 July 1993 (injured); and UNB 26-29 June 1994. Apparent hybrids with Eurasian Wigeon have been recorded (see preceding species account).

Canvasback: S&H (1979) considered this duck "fairly common on freshwater lakes...uncommon on coastal bays." It is now decidedly uncommon, occurring primarily on fresh water; 36 at Victoria Pond (SARM) 4 December 1994 was a recent high count. One summer record: SJC 13 June 1987.

Redhead: Three family groups at BC 28 June 1993 provided the county's first confirmed nesting records; nine adults were observed there 1 June 1995. A pair at SJM 14 May 1993, followed by two groups of juveniles on

1 July 1993, indicated nesting there, as well. Fall migrants are exceptional before the latter half of September.

Ring-necked Duck: This diving duck is fairly common in winter at deep reservoirs, generally away from the immediate coast. Ring-necked Duck is rare at SJM and very rare at coastal estuaries.

Lesser Scaup: Four unseasonal records: one or two at BC 4-18 August 1985; UNB 11 August 1988; HCP 31 May 1993; and SJM "late April" to 12 August 1993.

Greater Scaup: This duck is regularly encountered in small numbers at coastal estuaries, often with Lesser Scaup. While Greater Scaup is undoubtedly very rare on fresh water, a near lack of inland records since 1980 may reflect a relative lack of effort to detect this species among flocks of Lesser Scaup at inland reservoirs. A male (presumably a single bird) summered at BC in 1983, 1984, 1986 and 1987.

King Eider: Four winter records: HBP 18 December 1982-31 January 1983 (female); LNB 26 December 1982-16 January (female); Seal Beach Pier 13-31 December 1991 (immature male); and Aliso Pier 23 December 1995 (*; female or immature male).

The LNB bird was reported again 18 June 1983, and the Aliso Pier bird may have been re-sighted at HBP 28 December 1995; written details were never submitted on these birds, however, and we consider the sightings equivocal. The Seal Beach bird apparently moved up the coast and was last recorded at Redondo Beach in "early June" 1992 (KLG).

Harlequin Duck: Two acceptable records: a female at LNB 25-26 November 1990, and a male believed to have wintered (possibly becoming resident) between BC and Huntington Harbour from 1984/85 to 1994/95. This bird was seen annually from 1984/85 to 1987/88, in 1989/90, and again (taken to be the same bird) 3-6 January 1995; the earliest arrival date was 27 September 1985 and the latest definite report was 1 June 1985. In 1989/90 and 1995, the bird was tame and associating with domestic ducks in the private waterways of Huntington Harbour, where it may have become resident.

An unsubstantiated report of three at Harlequin Ducks at UNB 5 January 1978 was originally published in *Western Tanager* 44(6):6 and included in S&H (1979).

Oldsquaw: Over 20 records since 1980, but unrecorded some years. Most recent records are of birds flying offshore or remaining where originally found for less than a week. A female "unable to fly" summered at Newport Beach in 1965 (not graphed, dates unspecified).

Black Scoter: Occurs almost annually, with many records pertaining to birds flying offshore or remaining where originally found for less than a week. Nine at HBP 17-19 January 1979 was a notable concentration. Two early fall records at HBP: 6 October-12 November 1973, and 31 October-19 November 1994. One summer record: BC 12-18 June 1992.

Surf Scoter: Three inland records: SARA 17 March 1983; SJC 15 November 1987; and a remarkable flock of ten at OCNC 13 April 1989, one remaining to 14 April.

White-winged Scoter: Willett (1933) termed this scoter a "very common winter visitant along coast" of southern California. It was irregularly rare to fairly common in late fall/winter through the 1970s, with a notable concentration of 15 to 32 at HBP 2 December 1979-3 February 1980. It has been rare since the mid-1980s, and has been missed altogether some years. Three late spring/summer records: BC 11 July 1981; Aliso Pier 3 July 1988; and two off NP 16 June 1990. Two inland records: OCNC 20 November 1984-19 March 1985, and SJC 29 November 1987.

Common Goldeneye: S&H (1979) called this diving duck "uncommon" along the coast, "rare on fresh water." It has been rare along the coast and very rare inland since at least 1980; eight at BC 28 December 1991 was a recent high count. Two summer records: BC 12 May-1 July 1932 (Willett 1933), and UNB "late June" to 4 August 1991.

Barrow's Goldeneye: A female was shot at BC 5 January 1901 (#LACM 5306), and a female was present at IRP 8 December 1984-17 February 1985.

Bufflehead: Three late spring records: SARA 10-14 May 1985; BC 19 May 1988; and SJM 7 May 1995. One summered at BC "mid-June" to 27 August 1991.

Hooded Merganser: Records average approximately four or five per year and appear to be increasing; most occur away from the immediate coast. High counts include 12 at YRP in February 1994, and 17 in Tustin 18 December 1994. Four late records: Tustin 30 March 1990; four at UNB 31 March 1990 with one remaining until 21 April; UNB 13 April 1991; and one remaining in Tustin until 8 April 1995.

Common Merganser: One at Yorba Regional Park 14 April 1988 was late for spring. A female, apparently summering, was at SARA 26 July-12 August 1995. A very high total of 214 was at SJC 23-24 January 1988. Exceptional coastal counts include nine at BC 1 January 1989, 17 at SBNWR 11 January 1989, and 13 at SJM 7 February 1991 (RAE, MAP).

Red-breasted Merganser: This duck of coastal waters is most common at BC, where fall/winter counts sometimes exceed 100. Ten freshwater records since 1982, with an exceptional concentration of up to seven at SARA 2 February-1 April 1988.

Ruddy Duck: This small diving duck is an uncommon but widespread breeder, utilizing emergent vegetation bordering ponds and reservoirs deep enough to allow effective foraging. It is an abundant winter visitor, occurring primarily near the coast and at large inland reservoirs.

Turkey Vulture: Nests primarily in and around the Cleveland National Forest, but may also occupy rocky canyons closer to the coast, such as Aliso Canyon (Gallagher 1993). S&H (1979) reported nesting in Laguna Canyon, and the species may still nest in the San Joaquin Hills. Substantial winter roosts exist in lowland eucalyptus groves (e.g., between 1986 and 1990, RRV observed up to 350 at Turtle Rock, Irvine, with numbers peaking in December).

California Condor: Formerly a rare winter visitor to the Santa Ana Mountains. Swarth (1908) found remains of one at UTC in September 1908. Pequegnat (1951) published the following records from the Santa Ana Mountains: one or two on 8 October 1937; two on 14 November 1937; one on 14 February 1938; and two during the fall of 1940.

Osprey: Nest record at Laguna Beach 5 March 1895 (Willett 1912). Nesting is not known in recent times, but single birds and at least one pair have exhibited preliminary nesting behavior at Irvine Lake and Newport Bay, including a single bird that built a nest on the mast of a boat at LNB "around 1980" (Gallagher 1993).

White-tailed Kite: S&H (1979) summarized this raptor's remarkable history in California. The status fluctuates markedly over large geographic areas in long term cycles that are at least partially linked to availability of its primary prey, the California Vole (*Microtus californicus*). During periods of relative abundance, kites are uncommon during the breeding season and fairly common during fall and winter, roosting in groups of 30 or more at locations such as SJM, BC and Thomas Riley Wilderness Park. The local (and regional) population dipped during the 1980s and early 1990s, a period when the species was rare during the breeding season and rare to uncommon during fall and winter.

Mississippi Kite: A sub-adult was at HCP 5-11 June 1989.

Bald Eagle: Davis (1897) documented nesting of "Southern" Bald Eagle (*H.l. leucocephalus*) at an unspecified locale in 1895 and 1896; Willett (1933) identified this spot as being "near Laguna." A juvenile was collected at a nest in Laguna Canyon 8 May 1927 (#MVZ 68006). Through the mid-1970s, this eagle was a very rare in fall and winter along the coast, particularly at UNB, with a few records from the interior foothills.

Bald Eagles have been recorded only four times since 1975: PT 29 November 1986; UNB 29 January 1989; a wing-tagged bird at UNB 3 February 1990 (apparently released at Santa Catalina Island); and UNB 16 March 1994.

Northern Harrier: This raptor is primarily an uncommon winter visitor to marshes, grasslands, rangelands, and broken scrub; it is occasionally encountered in the mountains. A few pairs nest in the San Joaquin Hills and, possibly, in and around Rancho Santa Margarita.

Sharp-shinned Hawk: This small accipiter is a fairly common migrant and winter visitor. Two summer records: SORP 3 July 1988, and UNB 9 July 1988.

Cooper's Hawk: This medium-sized accipiter breeds uncommonly in riparian woodlands and oaks, rarely in parks and other developed areas; approximately 40 nesting pairs are known (Gallagher 1993). Cooper's Hawk is fairly common September through mid-March.

Red-shouldered Hawk: This buteo is a common resident of oak and sycamore woodlands of the lowlands and foothills, and is a familiar sight along road shoulders and at the edges of developed areas. Only occasional dispersing birds are known from the higher mountains (PHB pers. comm.).

Broad-winged Hawk: Two acceptable records: DBSP 11 December 1985, and an adult at SJM 6 November 1994. #LACM 100700 is labeled "Orange County," but the origin and date are unreliable (KLG pers. comm.).

Swainson's Hawk: Historically more common, with numerous nest records from neighboring counties. All recent records are of light-phase birds. Ten spring records since 1987, including an exceptionally early migrant in Irvine 13 February 1994; four over UCI 5 April 1990 was a high count. Five acceptable recent fall records: Loma Ridge 19 October 1993; Irvine fields 27 October 1993; SJM 16 October 1994; SJM 29 October 1994; and IRP 11 November 1995. #LACM 99696 is labeled "Orange County," but the origin and date are unreliable (KLG pers. comm.).

Zone-tailed Hawk: Approximately 20 total records, some of which must pertain to returning birds; roughly half have occurred since 1993 as part of an apparent regional incursion noted north to Santa Barbara County. Only one (IRP 20 December 1992) has been rejected by the CBRC, although many were never submitted for review. One spring record: SORP 30 April 1994 (*). Three early fall records: Laguna Beach 15 August 1993, remaining into December (*); Chiquita Canyon at SJC 18 September 1994 (PHB; ø); and Hicks Canyon 12 September 1994 (*).

Red-tailed Hawk: The widespread "Western" Red-tailed Hawk (*B.j. calurus*) nests commonly in expansive grasslands and rangelands of the lowlands and foothills, uncommonly closer to the margins of settled areas, and rarely in the mountains. A marked influx of non-breeding birds is noted September through March. Western red-tails are highly variable, with underparts and wing linings ranging from light to very dark.

"Harlan's" Red-tailed Hawk (*B.j. harlani*) has been recorded twice: PT 29 December 1985; UNB/SJM 14 January-3 March 1990, and what is presumed to be the same individual at SJM 26 December 1990. Additional subspecies may occur.

Ferruginous Hawk: Wintering birds were formerly considered at least "fairly common" in open country (cf. Willett 1933); now, wintering habitat exists for approximately 10 birds per year (PHB pers. comm.). Two early records: TRNC 21 September 1988, and UCI 1 October 1988.

Rough-legged Hawk: S&H (1979) described this hawk as a "rare winter visitor, November-March, somewhat irregular." Widespread losses of open grasslands and rangelands have apparently led to the Rough-legged Hawk's decline in the county and region. Since 1976, it has been recorded only twice by experienced observers: BC 23 December 1984-11 January 1985, and SBNWR 26 November 1994 (JAC). A buteo photographed at SJM 7 December 1994 was reported as a Rough-legged, but the photograph was misplaced before the identification was confirmed.

Golden Eagle: Up to four pairs may nest in the Santa Ana Mountains and Chino Hills in a given year, usually without success (PHB pers. comm.). Historic nesting locales known to PHB include Laguna Niguel, San Juan Capistrano, Arroyo/Plano Trabuco and Lemon Heights. Occasional wanderers and wintering birds are found away from breeding areas.

American Kestrel: This small falcon is the county's most abundant and widespread nesting raptor, with a local resident population estimated to exceed 250 pairs (Gallagher 1993). Kestrels are most common in open grasslands, but can be found nesting even in the middle of urban areas with seemingly minimal foraging habitat nearby.

Merlin: One at Dana Point 20 September 1991 was an early fall migrant; the latest spring record is one at BC 22 April 1994. Two records of pale birds identified as apparent "Prairie" Merlins (*F.c. richardsonii*): a female at San Juan Capistrano 25 October 1994, and a male in Irvine 22 November 1995. Three records of the "Black" Merlin (*F.c. suckleyi*): Peter's Canyon 29 November-22 December 1988; what is taken to be a returning bird at YRP 15-17 February 1993, 24 January 1995, and 19 January 1996; and Silverado Canyon 15 April 1995.

Peregrine Falcon: The subspecies are not reliably separated in the field except by color bands, wing tags, etc. Most records refer to the "American" Peregrine Falcon (*F.p. anatum*), a race whose genetic integrity has been compromised through intensive recovery efforts involving introduction of birds from other races. Starting in the 1940s, pesticide poisoning, habitat loss, and egg collection caused widespread declines in *anatum* populations, including extirpation of the local breeding population. Previously, egg sets were taken at Corona del Mar 23 April 1922 (WFVZ 80424) and Dana Point 8 May 1927 (WFVZ 107984); PHB (pers. comm.) knows of historic nesting sites at Williams, Black Star and San Juan canyons, and two sites each at or near Santiago and Laguna canyons.

Since the mid-1980s, records of *anatum* have increased greatly owing to a ban on the pesticide DDT, successful recovery efforts, and continued protection of coastal estuaries. In 1992 and 1993, young were produced at an Orange County coastal locale, but a new pair at this site failed to produce young in 1994 and 1995 (JL pers. comm.). PHB captured an American Peregrine at SJC 14 January 1995 that was banded as a first-year bird on 7 September 1992 at the Marin Headlands in northern California. #UCLA 6348 is an immature female collected at BC 8 January 1921 labeled *F.p. pealei*; CMW and RAH independently found this specimen consistent with *anatum*.

The highly migratory "Tundra" Peregrine (*F.p. tundrius*), which breeds on Alaska's north slope, should occur regularly during migration and possibly during winter (PHB pers. comm.). Two records of *tundrius* birds banded as nestlings on the Coleville River, Alaska: one banded in 1994 was found dead at John Wayne Airport in Santa Ana 6 November 1994, and a female banded in 1988 was observed consorting with a male anatum at the nesting locale discussed previously from "March" through 15 April 1995 (JL pers. comm.).

Prairie Falcon: Fall and winter records have decreased steadily since 1980, presumably due to loss of grasslands. Since 1991, a pair has been observed periodically throughout the year in the vicinity of upper Gypsum Canyon, but nesting has not been confirmed. An egg set was collected from this general area ("Santa Ana Canyon") 15 April 1922 (WFVZ 63153).

California Quail: This widespread quail is most abundant in scrub and chaparral of the coastal hills, interior foothills and lower mountain canyons. In the higher mountains, Pequegnat (1951) reported occasional sightings up to 4000 feet throughout the year, and RAH observed 20 near the Main Divide at UTC on 26 August 1995.

Mountain Quail: Fairly common resident of the higher mountains, occurring as low as approximately 2000 feet. A shy bird, Mountain Quail may be quite difficult to locate except during the spring, when courting males make their presence known with booming calls that carry exceptionally well through the mountain canyons.

Yellow Rail: This rail was probably a regular winter visitor to coastal estuaries historically, and reports from UNB occasionally surface, but there is only one confirmed record: UNB 12 December 1896 (Osburn 1911).

Black Rail: Formerly a rare resident/winter visitor at UNB, with two acceptable records there since 1980: 29 January 1983 (JCW), and 12 March 1993 (RZ).

Clapper Rail: UNB and SBNWR support the last major populations of the endangered "Light-footed" Clapper Rail (*R.l. levipes*), which Bangs (1899) originally described from UNB. Due to predation by the non-native Red Fox (*Vulpes vulpes*), high tide counts at SBNWR dropped to a low of two individuals in 1985, prompting the U.S. Fish and Wildlife Service to step up resource management efforts there, including provision of nesting platforms and Red Fox control (Zembal 1993). From 1985 to 1993, the total number of pairs in the county increased from 100 to 207 (Gallagher 1993).

In spring 1982, RZ (pers. comm.) observed five pairs at SJM west of Campus Drive, with "additional pairs across Campus Drive [to the east] in the marsh off Carlson Avenue." In spring 1992, he found an advertising male at SJM.

Five SDNHM specimens were taken 20 April 1931 at "Balboa Lagoon" (Balboa Island/LNB, where tidal wetlands once existed). S&H (1979) considered this a "fairly common resident" at BC, but only small numbers have been observed there in recent years (high count of three on 20 August 1994). The U.S. Fish and Wildlife Service intends to eventually re-establish Clapper Rails at BC and possibly other local coastal estuaries.

Virginia Rail: This rail is an uncommon winter visitor and, presumably, a rare breeder. Gallagher (1993) reported summer records from VPB, PCRP and BR; RAE reported three at Laguna Lakes 19 June 1992, and one at Cañada Gobernadora 1 August 1995; JEP observed a juvenile at SJM 31 July 1993.

Sora: Grinnell (1898) considered the Sora a "more or less common resident" in the Los Angeles Basin "wherever there are swampy lands overgrown with marsh grasses and tules." G&M (1944) termed it a "common and widely distributed" breeder statewide. In Orange County, Sora is now a rare, local breeder and fairly common winter visitor. In recent years, nesting has been confirmed at Cañada Gobernadora, the CSUF Arboretum and SARA, with probable nesting at SJM, PCRP, Laguna Lakes and other locales.

Common Moorhen: S&H (1979) characterized this species as primarily a fall and winter visitor, with nesting unknown. Moorhens are now known to nest locally each year at scattered freshwater marshes, including Laguna Lakes, SJM and UNB (Big Canyon).

American Coot: Breeds fairly commonly to commonly at freshwater wetlands with emergent vegetation. In fall and winter, coots are abundant at freshwater ponds and reservoirs, feeding in adjacent turfed areas at golf courses, urban parks and similar settings.

Sandhill Crane: S&H (1979) considered this crane a "very rare migrant or winter visitor" in the early 1900s; this seems uncertain, however, since Grinnell (1898) described "large, V-shaped flocks" over the Los Angeles area during spring and fall migrations, and Willett (1933) mentioned aggregations of 25-30 and 100 near Newport in the late 1890s.

Six recent records: one flying over Seal Beach 25 January 1981; five flying over UCI 2 December 1986 (RAH); UNB/SJM 27-28 January 1990; two at SJC 20 December 1990-12 January 1991, one remaining to 23 February 1991; one flying over SORP 25 February 1991; and one east of San Juan Capistrano 16-17 December 1995.

Black-bellied Plover: When ponds at SJM are partially flooded in fall, this plover may occur there in substantial numbers (e.g., 70 on 27 August 1994). Influxes of this and other shorebirds at SJM often coincide with high tide, when the rising water level at nearby UNB forces birds off the mudflats there. The most consistent inland wintering locale is SARA, where approximately 10-30 have wintered each year since 1984/85; up to 52 there in October/November 1993 was a high count.

American Golden-Plover: Relatively few observers distinguished between this and the following species until shortly before the AOU "split" them in 1994. Although knowledge of the relevant field marks separating the two species was incomplete until the late 1980s, we consider some earlier records reliable.

Since 1982, at least 11 American Golden-Plovers have been found along the coast, at SJM, and in grassy fields near the coast. One inland record: SARA 19 October 1982. An exceptionally early golden-plover in El Toro (Lake Forest) 29 June 1978 (G&D 1981) was not identified to race.

Taking the two species together, S&H (1979) considered golden-plover to be an "uncommon fall migrant on coastal mudflats (regular at UNB, BC); rare winter visitor." Neither species of golden-plover has occurred at UNB or BC with any regularity since at least 1980.

Pacific Golden-Plover: Before this and the preceding species were "split" by the AOU, wintering golden-plovers (presumably Pacific) were recorded at or near UNB on the 1963, 1976 and 1977 coastal CBCs, with a high count of 11 on 27 December 1963. A flock of three to 16 Pacific Golden-Plovers has wintered at SBNWR annually since 1980/81, arriving as early as 7 August 1993 (one bird) and departing as late as 8 May 1983 (eight birds). Two in Huntington Beach 7 April 1994 may have wintered locally apart from the SBNWR flock. Non-wintering fall migrants are rare and irregular, and have been recorded only as far inland as SJM.

Snowy Plover: Once common in southern California, the "Western" Snowy Plover (*C.a. nivosus*) showed some evidence of decline by the time of Willett (1933). S&H (1979) called it a "fairly common resident" with nesting known from BC, UNB and Seal Beach. A downy chick taken at Laguna Beach 8 May 1927 (#MVZ 68002) indicates historic nesting there, as well.

Nesting is currently limited to BC (at least five nesting pairs in 1995; recent high count of 11 pairs in 1989) and the SARM Least Tern nesting preserves. Two nesting pairs were found at SARM in 1993, with a high count of 21 on 23 September 1993 (JEP); up to ten were present there in summer 1994 but nesting was not detected (LRH). Migrants are very rare at SJM in late summer and early fall, and moderate numbers occur up and down the coast during winter (cf. Page et al. 1986). Two inland records of fall migrants at SARA: two on 13 August 1982, and one on 2 September 1988.

Semipalmated Plover: Uncommon to fairly common at coastal estuaries during winter, becoming common during migration periods. Individuals may occasionally summer on the coast, but June records may also reflect passage of late spring or early fall migrants. Semipalmated Plover is an uncommon to fairly common migrant at SJM, lower SDC, and SARA, occasionally occurring in winter.

Killdeer: This vocal plover is a ubiquitous resident of flood control channels, gravelly streambeds, agricultural fields and other open areas in the lowlands and foothills. Killdeer may nest some distance from water, often surprisingly close to humans.

Mountain Plover: This bird of open fields was recorded annually on coastal CBCs from 1956 to 1973, with a high count of 1156 on 26 December 1957; counts typically exceeded 100 through the 1960s. Four were collected in Seal Beach 15-16 December 1953 (#CSULB 390, 392-394). Substantial flocks continued to winter in open fields and crop lands in and around Irvine through the mid-1980s, with a high count of 120 in 1980/81. The last consistent wintering locale was the El Toro Marine Base, where a few birds could still be found through 1986/87. Three records since then: 12 at SBNWR 30

December 1990; a juvenile at San Clemente 9 October 1991; and 42 at the Seal Beach Naval Weapons Station 30 December 1995.

American Oystercatcher: After two American Oystercatchers were reported at CCSP 23 May (RD), two birds showing plumage characteristics of this species were found between CCSP and Crescent Point in Laguna Beach 3-5 September 1995. Jehl (1985) examined oystercatchers in Baja California and described the relative frequency of hybridization between American and Black oystercatchers, establishing a character index that classified the range of variation in 10 plumage characters evident in adult birds (in the hand or very well seen). Distant observations on 5 September 1995 suggested to RAH that the birds were near the dark extreme of *H.p. frazari* (the subspecies of American Oystercatcher found in northwestern Baja California), perhaps falling outside of an acceptable range of introgression. As such, we do not presently accept these records as definitely pertaining to American Oyster-catcher.

Subsequently, birds showing American Oystercatcher field marks were again reported at Crescent Point in Laguna Beach 29 January 1996 (*). This time, an adult bird consistent with "pure" *frazari* was part of a flock that also included a Black Oystercatcher and two immatures that appeared to be hybrids (one mostly American, the other mostly Black). These birds, some of which were apparently re-sighted between Laguna Beach and Dana Point through 16 March 1996, may have represented a family group; the possibili-ty of extralimital nesting warrants consideration.

Black Oystercatcher: Seldom recorded before 1991, this oystercatcher is now nearly regular during fall and winter. High counts include 16-19 at Seal Beach 4-13 January 1996 and 12 at Laguna Beach 27 January 1996. Non-breeders probably summer locally, but the lone summer record is one at Newport Beach 8 July 1992. As noted in the preceding species account, apparent hybrids with American Oystercatcher have been observed in the county.

Black-necked Stilt: Common resident found at coastal estuaries, SJM and SARA, with significant use of earthen flood control channels and other marginal wetland areas. At estuaries, stilts show a preference for areas influ-enced by fresh water. Numbers are augmented by birds from outside the county in fall and winter, but the timing and magnitude of this influx are poorly known.

American Avocet: This elegant shorebird is a common resident that nests primarily at coastal estuaries and SJM/lower SDC. Although their nesting requirements are similar, avocets nest at far fewer sites than Black-necked Stilts in the county and region.

Greater Yellowlegs: Fairly common migrant and uncommon to fairly common winter visitor. Most summer records are from the coast, some of these probably pertaining to late spring and early fall migrants. Inland, up to five summered at SARA in 1985.

Lesser Yellowlegs: Rare to uncommon spring migrant and uncommon to fairly common fall migrant, with the greatest concentrations typically occurring at SJM. Lesser Yellowlegs is a rare, regular winter visitor, occurring primarily near the coast. Two records of early fall migrants: DBSP 23 June 1984, and SJM 4 July 1994.

Solitary Sandpiper: Ten records of spring migrants, seven since 1987. Records average approximately four per fall, with few records of adults; 10-12 fall migrants in 1989 was exceptional. Early records include one adult at SARA 16 July 1982, and two to three adults at SJM 20-29 July 1994. Three records of late fall migrants: SARA 15 October 1982; SARA 17 October 1989; and VPB 20 October 1991.

Willet: The graphed freshwater status excludes SJM and lower SDC, where small numbers occur somewhat sporadically throughout the year (mainly in fall, but with a spring push evident primarily in April). Juveniles are rare at SARA during fall migration.

Wandering Tattler: This denizen of the rocky shoreline is an uncommon winter visitor, with somewhat greater numbers passing through during fall and particularly spring migration periods. One at SARM 8-9 June 1987 was apparently a late spring migrant. Two remained at Crescent Bay in Laguna Beach through the summer of 1994 (KLP).

Spotted Sandpiper: This sandpiper is a fairly common winter visitor, with somewhat greater numbers present during migration periods. Since the late 1980s, up to a few pairs have been detected nesting along the upper Santa Ana River. Recent summer observations of single birds along SDC and UNB suggest possible nesting at those locations, as well (Gallagher 1993).

Whimbrel: Along the coast, this is a fairly common fall migrant and winter visitor; it is a fairly common spring migrant at wetlands and fields county-wide. Whimbrels are rare inland during fall and winter, with only two records of fall migrants at SARA: 5 September 1985 (DRW), and 23 July 1995 (BED).

Long-billed Curlew: This large shorebird is a fairly common migrant and winter visitor at the larger coastal estuaries, with a few non-breeders remaining through the summer. Small numbers occur regularly during fall and winter at SJM and fields within a few miles of the coast (e.g., MRP, Fairview Park in Costa Mesa); curlews are rare and sporadic farther inland.

Marbled Godwit: Foraging birds are fairly common at SJM, MRP and grassy fields up to a few miles inland during fall and winter, frequently with Long-billed Curlews. Small numbers of fall migrants occur irregularly at SARA during fall; the species is unrecorded there during winter and spring.

Ruddy Turnstone: Uncommon to fairly common during migration and winter at large coastal estuaries. Ten or fewer usually summer at BC. High summer counts include 28 at BC 3 July 1984; 24 at UNB 14 June 1985; and 30 at BC 4 July 1985. Two inland records: SARA 22 September 1983, and SJM 16-17 September 1995.

Black Turnstone: Fairly common migrant and winter visitor, occurring primarily along the rocky coastline from Newport Beach south. Rare at coastal estuaries. One at SJM 8 October 1992 was a short distance inland.

Surfbird: This bird of the rocky coastline is uncommon to fairly common during spring migration, with exceptional counts of 200 at DBSP 1 April 1964 and 122 at SARM 4 April 1985 (LRH). One at UNB 21 April 1990 was away from its usual habitat.

Red Knot: Graph shows the general status at BC, where numbers have been increasing during all seasons; they are presently fairly common to common there fall through spring, with a high count of 94 on 18 April 1992. In 1993 and 1994, summer numbers at BC hovered above 20, with peak counts of 58 on 3 June 1994 and 55 on 24 June 1994.

Five fall records and one winter record away from coastal estuaries: SARA 11 August 1982; seven between UNB and Newport Harbor High School athletic fields 30 January-28 February 1983; SARA 16-18 September 1983; SARA 23-27 September 1983, with two or three birds observed on 27 September (considered one record); four at SJM 30 July 1993; and six at SJM 27 August 1994.

Sanderling: From fall through spring Sanderling flocks are familiar landscape elements at the surf-line and at coastal estuaries. Two inland records from SARA: 19-21 October 1984 (juvenile), and 28 July 1995 (adult).

Semipalmated Sandpiper: Records have averaged two or three per fall since 1984, with only four records of adults; most records are from SJM and SARA. Three early records of adults: BC 7 July 1981 (the first county record); UNB 10 July 1988; and SARA 15 July 1988. Three late records of juveniles at SJM: 27-28 September 1992; 2 October 1992; and 23 September 1995.

Western Sandpiper: Abundant fall migrant at coastal estuaries, SJM and SARA. Wintering birds and spring migrants are abundant at coastal estuaries, fairly common to common at SJM, and rare to uncommon and localized inland. Exceptional numbers were present at BC during late spring 1994, with a high count of at least 85 on 3 June; nearly all were in basic plumage.

Little Stint: An adult was at SJM 25-28 July 1992. The CBRC narrowly rejected a report of an adult at UNB 9 July 1988, determining that Red-necked Stint (*Calidris ruficollis*) could not be ruled out.

Least Sandpiper: This "peep" is common and widespread during fall migration but is greatly outnumbered by Western Sandpiper, particularly along the coast. Wintering birds and spring migrants are common at coastal estuaries, uncommon to fairly common inland. Western Sandpiper routinely outnumbers Least by a factor of ten or more on the coastal CBC, but the inland CBC often tallies two to several times more Least Sandpipers than Westerns. Two unseasonal records: BC 11 June 1985, and SBNWR 26 May 1991.

White-rumped Sandpiper: An adult was at SJM 9-13 September 1990.

Baird's Sandpiper: Records average approximately three per fall, with only a few records of adults; a total of 13 or 14 in 1989 was unusual. Two early records of adults: two at SARA 16 July 1982, and one at Seal Beach 8 July 1989. Three acceptable late fall records of juveniles: SJM 26-28 October 1990; SJM 4 October 1991; and San Clemente 9 October 1991. S&H (1979) considered Baird's Sandpiper a "rare spring migrant," but detailed supporting evidence would be required to accept a record outside of fall migration.

Pectoral Sandpiper: Two acceptable spring records: UNB 29 April 1972, and two at SJM 16 April 1989. Fall migrants, almost all juveniles, often number between 15 and 25, with a high seasonal total of at least 33 in 1988 (including 21 at SARA 25 September). Poor habitat conditions at SJM can lower the county's seasonal total by half or more. Two records of early fall migrants: two at HCP 12 August 1984 (age/sex unknown), and an adult on SDC 13 August 1995. One lingered at SJM until 1 December 1988.

Sharp-tailed Sandpiper: Two records of fall migrants: a juvenile was at UNB 13-14 October 1986, and an adult (especially rare in California) was at SJM 29 September-8 October 1992.

Dunlin: This sandpiper is a common migrant and winter visitor at coastal estuaries. The freshwater graph reflects the status at SJM; elsewhere (e.g., SARA), Dunlins are uncommon from October through early November, with few records after mid-November.

Two late spring records: BC 11-16 June 1989, and one to two at Seal Beach 10-13 June 1990. Three summer records: UNB 8-15 July 1989; BC 4 July 1994; and BC 28 June-10 August 1995. One early fall record: UNB 24-29 August 1988.

Curlew Sandpiper: An adult molting out of alternate plumage was at UNB 5 September 1971.

Stilt Sandpiper: Thirteen records of fall migrants, eight occurring between 31 August and 20 September (most or all juveniles). Two earlier fall records of adults: SJM 25 July 1992, and SJM 13-14 August 1994. Three later fall records: SJM 17 October 1970; UNB 18 November 1972; and up to three at SJM 13 September-7 October 1995. Two winter records: BC 2 February-1 March 1982, and SJM 17-21 January 1995.

Ruff: Five fall records, at least four involving juveniles: Capistrano Beach 26 September-11 October 1966 (age unknown); SARA 5-12 September 1986; SARA 15 September 1987; SJM 21-30 September 1989; and SJM 21-22 October 1995. One winter record: SARM 31 December 1962.

Short-billed Dowitcher: Substantial numbers typically summer at UNB and BC, with a high count of at least 300 at BC in 1994. The freshwater graph represents the status at SJM, where this dowitcher is an uncommon to fairly common fall migrant. It is generally a rare fall migrant elsewhere inland, although juveniles are uncommon at SARA during August and early September.

Long-billed Dowitcher: This dowitcher is an abundant migrant and winter visitor, with occasional stragglers noted into early June. The largest numbers are found at large coastal estuaries, but concentrations may also be encountered well inland, particularly during fall migration.

Common Snipe: This secretive bird is an uncommon migrant and winter visitor, with a high count of approximately 35 along the lower Santa Ana River 8 December 1989. An early fall migrant was at SJM 29 July-3 August 1994.

Wilson's Phalarope: This fairly common transient is occasionally encountered in large numbers along the coast (e.g., 300 at BC on both 6 August 1985 and 15 July 1995). Two records of late fall migrants: UNB 16 November 1963, and two in Huntington Beach 27 November 1985.

Red-necked Phalarope: This phalarope is an uncommon to fairly common spring migrant and fairly common fall migrant. Better pelagic coverage would likely reveal this to be a common fall migrant far offshore (e.g., RAE observed 1000 between Newport and Santa Catalina Island 13 August 1991, and 300 there the following day). Spring migrants are rare close to shore and at coastal estuaries; fall migrants are generally uncommon in these areas. The rare/irregular "summer" status primarily reflects passage of late spring or early fall migrants; up to three that summered at BC during 1995 were exceptional. The freshwater graph primarily reflects the status at SJM.

Four records of early spring migrants or storm-blown wintering birds, including three in 1995: Anaheim Bay 2 February 1980 (#CSULB 5971); SJM 11 March 1995 (inland); up to four at BC 16-25 March 1995; and three at SBNWR 24-25 March 1995. Up to three late fall migrants were at BC 20-29 November 1986. Two winter records: coastal CBC 27 December 1963, and two off Huntington Beach 26 January 1986 (RWR).

Red Phalarope: Graph reflects the expected offshore status. Transients and winter visitors occur rarely in the nearshore waters and at coastal estuaries, often following storms. An early fall migrant was at BC 3 August 1995; ten at BC 10 November 1982 (LRH) was a high count. Six inland records: SJM 6 June 1982; lower SDC 21-26 July 1982 (early fall migrant); up to three at SARA 11-14 November 1982; two at HCP 12 November 1982; SJM 11 March 1995 (early spring migrant); and Fairview Park in Costa Mesa 12 March 1995 (early spring migrant).

Pomarine Jaeger: Fairly common well offshore, outnumbering Parasitic Jaeger by at least 20 to 1 (RRV in litt.); sighted rarely to uncommonly from shore.

Parasitic Jaeger: This fairly common transient and rare winter visitor is found primarily in the nearshore waters, exceptionally at coastal estuaries. Four summer records: HBP 26 July 1977; HBP 15 June 1978; HBP 12 July 1978; and one or two at NP 21-22 July 1992. One approximately seven miles inland at SJC 31 January 1988 was exceptional.

Long-tailed Jaeger: Three fall records of adults in alternate plumage, none definitely at sea: "San Clemente" 18 September 1959 (#WFVZ 43005); BC (grounded) 30 September 1987; and SARA 14 August 1988. This may be a rare, regular fall migrant far offshore.

South Polar Skua: One was observed approximately one mile off Huntington Beach 5 July 1992. One "near Catalina" 5 May 1982 was just outside of the area considered in this book (EAC pers. comm.).

Laughing Gull: Three May records: BC 29 May 1986; BC 19 May 1988; and two at UNB 9 May 1992. Six records in July and August: UNB 11 July 1981; BC 2 July 1984; UNB 22-25 July 1986; SARA 16 August-3 September 1988 (inland, where very unusual); UNB 29 July-21 August 1989; and off PP 3 July 1992. Three late fall/winter records: Huntington Beach 26 November 1969; off Newport 30 December 1979; and an inland record from SARA 23 February 1989 (JEP).

Franklin's Gull: Four spring records: two at BC 18 May 1983; one at BC 14 May 1989; one at SJM 7 May 1995; and one off NP 13 May 1995. One summer record: BC 17 July 1988. Records average two to three per fall, although it is missed some years; the vast majority are sub-adult. Two early fall records: SARA 23 September 1983, and off Newport 27 September 1986. Two winter records: Craig Regional Park 9-22 January 1989, and Huntington Beach 12 January 1995.

Little Gull: A first-year bird, apparently a spring migrant, was at YRP 25 March 1995 (*). Two were present at SARM during the same fall/winter: 22 November-21 December 1980 (adult), and 24 January 1981 (first-year bird).

Black-headed Gull: An adult (presumably a single bird) was recorded at SARM in successive years: 21 November 1980-25 February 1981, and 13 December 1981-26 January 1982. Formerly known as Common Black-headed Gull.

Bonaparte's Gull: Abundant winter visitor along the lower Santa Ana River, feeding at the sewage treatment plant on Ellis Avenue and roosting along the coast; representative approximate counts include 2500 on 29 March 1989 (LRH) and 2000 on 1 January 1995 (RAH). Inland, this gull is consistently common only at IL; winter storms bring small numbers to SARA. The vast majority of wintering birds are adults, while flocks of spring migrants along the coast include higher percentages of sub-adults (e.g., 65 passing north off NP 5 May 1995 were nearly all first-year birds).

Heermann's Gull: Non-breeders are uncommon to fairly common along the coast in late winter and spring. One inland record: Irvine Lake 15 December 1991.

Mew Gull: Fairly common migrant and winter visitor. Concentrations are primarily coastal, but substantial flocks also occur along the Santa Ana River and surrounding areas north to Santa Ana (e.g., 300 at Centennial Park, Santa Ana, 23 January 1989). Mew Gulls are rare and possibly regular along the river north of Santa Ana, and at inland locales away from the river.

Ring-billed Gull: This gull roosts abundantly along the coast from fall through spring, commuting daily to suitable foraging areas, including SARA, landfills and flooded fields. In summer, sub-adults roost fairly commonly along the coast and uncommonly to fairly commonly at SARA.

California Gull: This gull roosts abundantly along the coast from fall through spring, commuting daily to suitable foraging areas, including SARA, landfills and flooded fields. In summer, sub-adults roost fairly commonly along the coast and uncommonly to fairly commonly at SARA.

Herring Gull: S&H (1979) considered this gull "common" along the coast and "rare inland (dumps)," but Herring Gulls are now primarily found along the upper Santa Ana River and at landfills during the day, with typical daily counts in the range of 25 to 50. They are generally uncommon and local along the coast during the day; regular gathering locations include DBSP, Little Corona State Beach and the Balboa Peninsula at 18th Street.

Increased exploitation of inland resources by Herring, Western and other gulls in Orange County is consistent with ongoing changes in the winter ranges of many gull species throughout the West, as documented and discussed by Binford and Johnson (1995).

Thayer's Gull: Most records of this rare winter visitor pertain to first-year birds on the coast. One off Newport 6 May 1978 was late.

Lesser Black-backed Gull: An adult wintered at DBSP 27 December 1994-29 January 1995 (*). This bird's plumage was consistent with *L.f. graellsii.*

Yellow-footed Gull: One winter record of an adult that remained a short time at NP 9 January 1993.

Western Gull: Along the coast, this large gull is abundant fall through spring; non-breeders are common during the summer months. Two pairs of the common *L.o. wymani* successfully nested in flower pots on private piers at LNB in 1989 and 1990, and one pair nested there in 1992 (Gallagher 1993). The light-mantled northern subspecies, *L.o. occidentalis,* is a rare to uncommon winter visitor, with high counts of at least eight at DBSP 25 January 1995 (DRW) and at least six at SARM 19 January 1995 (JEP). Apparent Western X Glaucous-winged hybrids are occasionally encountered.

Western Gulls were formerly very rare inland, but are now regular and increasing along the Santa Ana River, at landfills and at certain reservoirs; up to 65 have been present at SARA in late summer/fall each year since 1990. A group of nine in an east Orange parking lot 5 March 1995 was unexpected.

Glaucous-winged Gull: This uncommon winter visitor roosts along the coast, often commuting inland to forage at landfills and other sites; most records are of first-year birds. Up to three or four can usually be found at SARA. One at SJM 19 August 1987 was early.

Glaucous Gull: Most records are of first-year birds; adults are unrecorded. Two spring records: DBSP 11 April 1965, and Newport Bay 18 April-9 May 1976. Six fall/winter records: UNB 15 March 1975; HBP 25 December 1981; UNB 27 December 1981-16 March 1982; SARA 9 November 1984 (early for the region); Seal Beach 9 December 1985 (JSB); and SARA 14 March 1990. An apparent hybrid (other species unknown) was at SARA 27 November 1990; an apparent Glaucous X Herring hybrid was at Huntington Beach 4-9 February 1991.

Black-legged Kittiwake: The graphed status is largely speculative; most should occur well offshore where observer coverage is light. Very rarely recorded onshore. An immature irregularly observed off NP 5-24 December 1995 was the first record since 17-19 February 1990.

Sabine's Gull: The graphed status is largely speculative; RRV (in litt.) reports up to 30 per day inside of San Clemente Island (San Diego County) during May, suggesting somewhat greater numbers in spring than the graph shows. Two summer records in 1992: Four off NP 7 July, and one off PP 19 July. One at Huntington Beach 3 November 1973 was slightly late and may have been sick. Three onshore records: SARA 15 September 1982; SARM (observed by RRV foraging at the Ellis Avenue sewage treatment plant) 19-30 October 1984; and SARA 15 October 1994. Two specimen records of first-year birds: one brought to a bird rehabilitator in Surfside 8 May 1985 (#CSULB 6397), and one in "San Clemente" 21 August 1959 (#WFVZ 43006).

Ivory Gull: An exhausted first-year bird seen by many and photographed at DBSP 5 January 1995 (*) represented a first state record.

Gull-billed Tern: Two adults were at BC 1-10 June 1995. S&H (1979) considered hypothetical an earlier sight record of one at BC 3 July 1964 (VP).

Caspian Tern: Caspian Terns first nested at BC in 1986, eight years after the California Department of Fish & Game created sandy islands there; the high count to date was at least 300 pairs in 1993. This tern forages uncommonly at inland water bodies, and can be fairly common at SARA in fall. On 29 May 1994 RAH and SGH watched two circle over the Main Divide at UTC then head toward the coast.

Royal Tern: S&H (1979) traced this tern's local status change from a "common or fairly common fall migrant and winter visitor" during the first half of the century to a "decidedly rare" fall migrant and winter visitor by the 1970s. Royal Terns first nested at man-made islands at BC in 1988; the high count there is 15 pairs in June 1996 (CTC pers. comm.). High counts in late fall/winter include up to 16 at SBNWR 12 January-4 March 1995, and 28 at SBNWR 29 November 1995.

Elegant Tern: The local and regional status has changed considerably in the past 50 years, as summarized in S&H (1979) and Collins et al. (1991). Elegant Terns were common post-breeding migrants until 1983, when birds began to show up at BC in spring and early summer to inspect sandy islands established there in 1978. Numbers at BC increased in subsequent years until 31 pairs nested there (largely unsuccessfully) in 1987 (Gallagher 1993). This is now a major breeding colony containing at least 4000 pairs in 1995 and 1996 (Collins 1996). The earliest arrivals were single birds at

DBSP 1 March 1995 and at Seal Beach 4 March 1995. One at DBSP 29-31 December 1988 was a very late straggler.

Elegant Terns forage primarily at estuaries and in the ocean within approximately two miles of land, but may be encountered much farther from shore (e.g., RAH observed two in the vicinity of Lausen Knoll, 14 miles southwest of Newport Beach, 22 May 1994). This tern is generally very rare at freshwater locales near the coast, but small numbers were sighted fairly regularly at SJM during late summer/early fall 1995. A high inland count was 20 at SJM 11 June 1992 (RAE).

Sandwich Tern: An adult has been recorded twice at BC: 29 June-16 July 1991 (end date per JCS), and 24 June-17 July 1995 (*). Collins (1996) presented persuasive evidence that these sightings likely pertain to a single bird, probably a female. In 1995, the Sandwich Tern paired with an Elegant Tern to produce one offspring. Interestingly, adults showing bill characteristics intermediate between Elegant and Sandwich terns (possibly first-generation hybrids and/or back-crossed individuals raised at BC in previous years) were observed at BC in 1995: one on 25 June (*) and a different individual on 4 July (*).

Common Tern: S&H (1979) considered this tern "common in May." Sightings of spring migrants have been rare since 1980, the birds apparently passing offshore for the most part; three or four off NP 5 May 1995 is a recent high count. In fall, typical high counts at BC range between 50 and 75; over 100 there on 27 August 1988 was exceptional. Second-year birds normally arrive at BC in late June, about a month ahead of adults. Fewer than ten fall migrants have been recorded inland at SARA and SJM. Four acceptable winter records: BC 31 December 1978; BC 25 January 1981; two at BC 6 January 1983; and Corona del Mar/Balboa Pier 4-5 January 1987.

Arctic Tern: Almost never seen from shore, but small numbers are regularly observed from boats in fall; the graphed spring status is speculative. An adult female taken at Laguna Beach 1 May 1915 (Pierce 1919; #MVZ 54555) was a very early spring migrant. G&D (1981) reported this specimen lost, but CC (in litt.) verified its presence at MVZ. Exceptional for both timing and location was one observed resting and foraging at BC 9 July 1994. One other onshore record of an oiled bird at DBSP 5 October 1980.

Forster's Tern: The first breeding records were at UNB and BC in 1986 (three pairs at each location). A pair also nested at SBNWR in 1990. Presently, Forster's Tern nests primarily at BC, with a recent count of at least 220 pairs in 1995 (CTC pers. comm.); smaller numbers nest at UNB. The species is fairly common and widespread at inland water bodies the year-round, with a push of migrants evident late August through September.

Least Tern: At one time, "California" Least Terns (*S.a. browni*) nested on sandy beaches from the tip of the Balboa Peninsula to the Los Angeles County line (Carter et al. 1992). Human commandeering of sandy beaches in southern and central California led to this tern's state and federal listing as endangered. Gulls and the introduced Red Fox (*Vulpes vulpes*) prey on Least Terns, as well as other species of tern and Black Skimmer; control of these predators is widely considered essential to the stability of Orange County's significant tern and skimmer nesting colonies. In 1993, Orange County's populations at SBNWR, BC, SARM and UNB accounted for 637 of approximately 2300 pairs known in California (LRH in litt.) An early arrival was at BC 29 March 1993.

Once nesting gets underway, small numbers of Least Terns forage daily at SARM and, during most years, at SJM. In addition, they are regularly encountered at golf course ponds and similar sites within a mile or two of the coast. Farther inland, birds occasionally forage at SARA, VPB, and reservoirs such as Sand Canyon and Oso; 12 adults and juveniles at Laguna Reservoir 9 July 1989 (DRW) was a high inland count.

Sooty Tern: Adults at BC 30 July 1994 (*) and 17 June-8 August 1995 (*) were the second and fourth state records. One at DBSP on the morning of 30 July 1995 presumably commuted there from BC (it was missed by birders at BC that morning). Remarkably, the county has hosted three inconclusive sightings of Gray-backed/Bridled/Sooty terns: San Clemente 13 August 1968; BC 5 August 1990; and BC 12 June 1993.

Black Tern: Numbers passing through the county have dropped off dramatically, as Willett (1933) considered this tern a "common migrant" in the region, and S&H (1979) considered it a rare spring and uncommon fall migrant. Three recent spring records from BC: 25 May 1987; 27 May 1994; and four on 29 April 1995. Fall records have averaged approximately three per year since 1980, most occurring at BC. Two late fall/winter records: Dana Point 25 November 1986, and Corona del Mar 4 December 1986 to NP 24 February 1987 (considered one record).

Black Skimmer: One at SARM 8 September 1962 was the first U.S. Pacific Coast record. This was a rare, irregular visitor, May to October, until fall of 1984 when ten were at BC, swelling to 43 the following spring, ten pairs nesting. As summarized by Collins and Garrett (1996), hundreds now regularly nest at BC and UNB, and six pairs nested at SBNWR in 1987.

Gazzaniga (1996) found that up to 200 skimmers winter regularly at SBNWR, and that some use this site as a staging area before dispersing elsewhere in winter. The birds arrive there in September, increase through November/December, then decrease through March. Skimmers banded at

BC have been recorded in winter as far north as San Mateo and Santa Barbara counties, and south to Ensenada and San Quintin, Baja California, Mexico (Gazzaniga 1996). Banded birds raised at BC have subsequently nested at SBNWR, in San Diego, and at Isla Montague, located in the Colorado River delta, Baja California (Collins and Garrett 1996).

The graphed freshwater status pertains to foraging areas within a mile or two of the coast; during this period, small numbers typically forage at SJM daily during early morning and late afternoon (a high count was 15 on 2 August 1994). Five records farther inland: SARA 27 September 1983; SARA 4 September 1993; Oso Reservoir 28 May 1995; SARA 22-27 August 1995; and SARA 29 October 1995.

Common Murre: Ainley et al. (1994) and Takekawa et al. (1990) documented an approximate 50 percent decrease in central California breeding pairs following a peak in 1982, the last year that substantial numbers were found in Orange County (e.g., 150 off Dana Point 13 February 1982, 80 off Newport Beach 29 July 1982). Murres presumably occur regularly far offshore late fall through early spring, but have been recorded only four times since 1984 (twice in 1995/96).

Pigeon Guillemot: Three acceptable records, all in summer: NP 7 July 1992; NP 9 July 1992 (potentially the bird observed two days previously); and PP 11 July 1993. Details are lacking for an unseasonal report of one at NP 10 January 1964 (S&H 1979).

Xantus' Murrelet: Very rarely seen from shore, with all definite records pertaining to the Channel Islands breeder, *S.h. scrippsi*. Murrelet sightings are often left unidentified to species, since Xantus' is not safely separable from Craveri's if poorly seen. Four June/July specimen records: Balboa Beach 1 July 1913 (#11684 SDNHM); off Corona del Mar 1 July 1933 (#SBCM 30590); Newport Beach 4 July 1969 (#SBCM 33773); LNB 24 July 1972 (#WFVZ 22763); and Huntington Beach 4 June 1979 (#CSULB 6083).

Craveri's Murrelet: Possibly regular well offshore in late summer/early fall. The status is muddled by limited offshore coverage and identification problems between Craveri's and Xantus' murrelets. Four acceptable records: two off PP 19 July 1992; one off PP 21 July 1992 (potentially one of the birds observed two days previously); one at NP 11 August 1993; and one between Lausen Knoll and Santa Catalina Island 8 October 1993.

Ancient Murrelet: Five of the county's 18 records of this irruptive alcid occurred in 1995/96, including a remarkable count of approximately 30 off NP 15 December 1995. One specimen record: Newport 22 January 1928 (#WFVZ 49248).

Cassin's Auklet: In the offshore waters, this small seabird is expected to be uncommon to fairly common from fall through spring, and possibly regular in summer. A total of 25 off NP during warm water conditions on 24 June 1993 was a high count, particularly for the inshore waters in summer. Three CSULB skeletons of birds washed up at BC provide additional data: 16 May 1974 (#4597), 23 May 1974 (#4605), and "June 1984" (#6674).

Rhinoceros Auklet: This alcid is expected to be an uncommon to fairly common winter visitor well offshore; the high count is at least 75 three miles off Newport Beach 24 February 1990 (LRH). Rhinoceros Auklets are typically visible only from boats, but may be seen uncommonly from shore during certain years.

Horned Puffin: One record of a weak bird at HBP 21 January 1966.

Band-tailed Pigeon: This large pigeon is a fairly common resident of the Santa Ana Mountains, and about 50-150 have occupied the Fullerton Hills during recent years. Occasional wanderers are observed in the foothills throughout the year, very rarely reaching the coastal plain in fall and winter. Pequegnat (1951) observed regular, "many fold" increases in the mountains from late October to mid-March, reporting a remarkable count of approximately 20,000 at Modjeska Springs 11 January 1941. The mountains still experience winter influxes of varying magnitude.

White-winged Dove: Four spring records: two at UNB 8 April 1961 (possibly lingering winter birds); OCNC 19 May 1979 (DRW); SARA 21 May 1983; and two at SARM 26 May 1992. Nearly annual in fall; seasonal totals of four in 1990 and 1995 were exceptional. Winter records are more unusual.

Mourning Dove: This dove is a widespread year-round resident. An influx is noted in fall and winter, a period when aggregations of 100 or more can be readily found in expansive open space areas.

Common Ground-Dove: Once casual, this tiny dove has expanded its local range steadily since the first definite breeding record at Anaheim in 1952 (Pyle and Small 1961). It is now fairly common and widespread on the coastal plain from SARM north, with small numbers scattered to the south and east.

Ruddy Ground-Dove: A female was at lower SJC, near DBSP, 4-5 November 1993 (*).

Black-billed Cuckoo: An immature fall migrant at Bartlett Park in Huntington Beach 4-6 October 1989 represented the thirteenth state record, and only the third south of Mono and Monterey counties.

Yellow-billed Cuckoo: Historically, the "Western" Yellow-billed Cuckoo (*C.a. occidentalis*) was a locally common summer resident and breeder in expansive riparian woodlands associated with the Santa Ana River (Schneider 1900b, Willett 1933), and possibly elsewhere. Habitat destruction, especially channelization of the Santa Ana River, led to its local extirpation. The only recent record was a spring migrant at San Juan Capistrano 21 June 1981.

Greater Roadrunner: This charismatic bird is a fairly common resident of coastal sage scrub, scrub/grasslands, and broken chaparral in the lowlands and foothills. It is, at best, uncommon in the mountains. Roadrunners are absent from many fragmented habitat patches, but single birds or pairs occasionally wander into unoccupied areas (e.g., SARA, SJM).

Groove-billed Ani: A fall migrant at OCNC 13-17 September 1978 was the second state record.

Barn Owl: Widespread throughout the lowlands and foothills, occurring even in urban areas. A scarcity of mountain meadows (for foraging) limits nesting opportunities for this owl in District 3, although dispersing birds are expected to pass through the mountains with some regularity (PHB pers. comm.).

Western Screech-Owl: This small owl is a common permanent resident of oak and riparian woodlands in the coastal hills, interior foothills and mountains. The estimated peak density is one or two pairs per half-mile of streambed habitat (Gallagher 1993).

Great Horned Owl: This large owl occupies a diversity of habitats from the coast to the mountains, and is regularly encountered along development edges. Nesting substrates include tall trees, cliffs and human structures.

Burrowing Owl: Grinnell (1898) considered the "Western" Burrowing Owl (*S.c. hypugaea*) an "abundant resident on the lowlands and mesas" of the Los Angeles basin. S&H (1979) called it a "fairly common resident...throughout coastal plain and foothills," noting an overall decline due to urbanization and ground squirrel control. Continued large-scale destruction and fragmentation of gently sloping grasslands has reduced the known population to a single pair near UCI and four or five pairs at SBNWR (PHB pers. comm.). Fall migrants and wintering birds are rare, the former sometimes occurring at unexpected locations (e.g., off PP 16 October 1994, Westminster Memorial Park 5 November 1994).

Spotted Owl: The "California" Spotted Owl (*S.o. occidentalis*) is a rare, local resident of steep, wooded mountain canyons. The only known birds are at UTC (pair last heard 14-15 May 1994). A specimen was collected in Silverado Canyon 24 August 1989 (#WFVZ 48019).

Long-eared Owl: Once considered common throughout lowland cismontane California (Cooper 1870, Sharp 1907, Dawson 1923, Willett 1933), this owl is now quite rare. Bloom (1994) found Long-eared Owls nesting locally in dense woodlands of the lower canyons of the Santa Ana Mountains and the southern foothills, primarily in Coast Live Oaks (*Quercus agrifolia*); all territories were at least one km from residential developments. In 1991 six active nests were found, four of which produced young; in 1992 twelve active nests were found, eleven of which produced young. A lack of sightings by PHB in 1994 and 1995 indicates that the local population fluctuates significantly year to year, although it seems unlikely that the species vacates the county entirely (PHB pers. comm.).

Long-eared Owls are very scarce lowland migrants, with only four records in recent times: PHB trapped and banded an adult at SJM in the early 1970s; one was found dead at UNB in late January or early February 1989 (mounted specimen at El Dorado Nature Center, Long Beach); individuals were in Corona del Mar 6 November 1990 and 11 November 1994.

Short-eared Owl: Willett (1933) called this a "common winter visitant" and reported a nest with two eggs "near Newport" 25 April 1928 (not graphed). G&D (1981) called one in Huntington Beach 10 July 1947 "the most recent summer record for the coast" of southern California (a pair has subsequently nested on Santa Barbara Island). S&H (1979) termed this owl an "uncommon winter visitor...occasionally common at concentration points such as SJM."

Short-eared Owl is now a rare, nearly regular fall migrant and winter visitor, most often seen at SJM, BC and UNB; a recent high seasonal total was seven or eight during fall 1994. A lingering bird or late spring migrant was at SBNWR 16 April 1995. Two early fall records: BC 7 September 1959, and SJM 11 September 1994. Fall migrants are occasionally noted flying over city parks and residential areas. PHB reports that individual birds have been observed periodically in grasslands on the north slope of Preusker Peak (SRAS) since the early 1970s; this is the only inland locale where Short-eared Owl is known to occur with any regularity.

Northern Saw-whet Owl: Pequegnat (1951) heard this owl on several occasions from 1940 to 1951, and the species is still found in the higher canyons of the Santa Ana Mountains. Since the first recent records in upper Silverado Canyon during March and April 1993, up to three or four have been found in upper Silverado, Harding and/or McVicker canyons each spring. Recorded twice in Huntington Beach residential neighborhoods: 17 December 1972, and a sick bird found in "October 1987" (#HCP, Shipley Nature Center).

Lesser Nighthawk: This goatsucker is an uncommon, localized breeder in the interior foothills. Recent high counts include "many dozens" at CHSP (Telegraph Canyon) 13 April 1980 (MAP), and 43 around SJC 13 July 1989. Pequegnat (1951) found birds up to 4000 feet, but recent records from the mountains are lacking.

Three records in spring and summer away from potential nesting habitat: HCP 17 May 1984; HCP 26 May 1991; ENC 31 May 1992 (WDG); and SJM 22 June 1995 (TEH). Since 1987, lowland fall records have averaged about two per year, many of these at SJM. Four winter records: Orange 3 December 1982; SJM 9 November 1984-24 February 1985; Anaheim 28 February 1990; and SJM "December" 1993 to 4 January 1994.

Common Nighthawk: A sick bird that died the next day was found on a roof in Orange 4 July 1983 (#LACM 101221).

Common Poorwill: Fairly common to common breeder in brushlands from the coastal hills to the mountains; Poorwills are probably regular in winter (cf. G&M 1944, AOU 1957) but inactivity makes detection difficult. Four specimen records are of the coastal breeding race *P.n. californicus*: San Clemente 10 March 1934 (#SDNHM 16523); Seal Beach 23 October 1969 (#CSULB 3979); Anaheim Hills 21 October 1985 (#WFVZ 35257); and Black Star Canyon 2 February 1961 (#WFVZ 23559).

One record of a spring migrant away from typical habitat: ENC 24 April 1983. In addition to the Seal Beach record listed above, the following records suggest that transients/dispersing birds pass through the lowlands with some regularity from mid-August through early November: Orange 8 October 1983; HCP 13 October 1986; HCP 19 September 1987; UCI 15 August 1989; one roosting on the ground at a shopping mall in Orange (!) 3-4 November 1993; HCP 9 October 1994; Huntington Beach (on a roof) 9 October 1995; and one observed flying out of Canyon Park in Costa Mesa 20 October 1995, rising high in the air to be mobbed by American Crows.

Black Swift: S&H (1979) mentioned sightings of spring and fall migrants "every few years" but did not elaborate. Eight acceptable May records, six since 1987; one at BC 10 June 1981 was late. Five acceptable fall records: male taken at San Juan Capistrano 10 September 1924 (Willett 1933; location of specimen unknown); Santa Ana Mountains 12 August 1940; Corona del Mar 10-11 August 1941; SJM 28 August 1982; and Santiago Peak 18 August 1984.

Chimney Swift: One acceptable record: four in Orange 16 June 1980 (BKS). Two summer/early fall records of *Chaetura* swifts probably pertain to this species: UCI 7 July 1973 (S&H 1979 p. 69), and two to four at SORP 15 June 1982 with one there 15 July 1982 (considered one record).

Vaux's Swift: This is an uncommon to fairly common transient county-wide; numbers detected vary from year to year. One at SRAS 23 March 1992 was probably an early spring migrant. Two winter records: 11 in Huntington Beach 24 February 1975 (21 February erroneously reported elsewhere), and three in Fullerton 13 January 1985. As noted by G&D (1981) a report of three Vaux's Swifts at UTC 13 August 1955 may have pertained to Chimney Swifts.

White-throated Swift: This is a fairly common resident found primarily in the vicinity of nesting colonies on steep cliffs and under large bridges in the foothills and mountains. Consistent and accessible viewing locations include SORP and the Oso Parkway bridge over the Arroyo Trabuco.

Broad-billed Hummingbird: Five records in fall and winter: TRNC 29-30 September 1982 (adult male); Mission Viejo 30 November-12 December 1987 (immature male); Orange 11 February 1991 (adult male); HCP 1 November 1994 (adult male); and MRP 14 October 1995 (immature male).

Black-chinned Hummingbird: This hummer breeds fairly commonly in and around wooded areas, and is locally common in expansive riparian forests of the lowlands and foothills. One in Fountain Valley 18 March 1994 was probably an early migrant. Two acceptable winter records: Westminster 29 January 1987, and CSUF Arboretum 23 January-26 February 1994.

Anna's Hummingbird: Abundant permanent resident, occupying a diversity of habitats from the coast to the highest mountains. Two records of apparent Anna's X Costa's hybrids: CCSP 18 April 1984, and Huntington Beach 16 September 1995.

Costa's Hummingbird: This hummingbird is a common summer resident in coastal sage scrub and chaparral communities. Small numbers winter regularly in lowland neighborhoods, with high seasonal estimates of 12 in 1984/85 and 1994/95. Pequegnat (1951) reported "numerous records of birds feeding on *Zauschneria californica* [*Epilobium canum*] as late as November 27," which suggested to him that "a few birds pass the winter" in native vegetation of the foothills and lower mountains.

Calliope Hummingbird: Pequegnat (1951) "[knew] little of this bird on the Santa Ana Mountains," listing only one definite record: Modjeska Springs 24 May 1940 (late). S&H (1979) considered it a "fairly common spring migrant in mountains, April-May." Limited observer coverage suggests that this hummer is a rare spring migrant through the Santa Ana Mountains, probably regular at higher elevations. Three at approximately 4500 feet in Silverado Canyon 8 April 1995 was a high daily count for recent years. One record from the coastal lowlands: Seal Beach 30 March 1993.

Rufous Hummingbird: Pequegnat (1951) did not distinguish Rufous from Allen's, considering the two hummingbirds "common in March, less common in April, and occasional as late as May 22." S&H (1979) termed Rufous a "fairly common migrant throughout county...abundant in mountains in spring migration around blooming manzanita." Spring migrants are now fairly common in the foothills and mountains, rare to uncommon in the coastal lowlands. Fall migrants are uncommon, occurring primarily in the interior. The status is somewhat speculative, especially in fall, due to difficulty separating many individuals from Allen's Hummingbird. One in South Laguna 27 January 1980 was probably an early spring migrant.

Allen's Hummingbird: The non-migratory *S.s. sedentarius*, first detected nesting in 1980, is a locally common resident in and around large eucalyptus stands near the coast and appears to be expanding into the interior of the county. The migratory *S.s. sasin* is not believed to nest in the county, but its status is difficult to ascertain since the subspecies are indistinguishable in the field. Migration is mostly coastal, particularly in fall.

Belted Kingfisher: This popular bird is a fairly common migrant and winter visitor from the coast to the foothills, and a rare, localized breeder. Gallagher (1993) reported nesting at IRP, VPB, SDC and SARA.

Lewis' Woodpecker: S&H (1979) considered this bird a rare and irregular transient and winter visitor, consistent with the present status. Earlier, Pequegnat (1951) termed it an "abundant winter visitant [in oaks] south of Ortega Road," but did not elaborate. At least 20 in the county during winter 1984/85 was a very high seasonal total for recent years. Birds typically depart by late April; the latest lingered in Santiago Canyon until 9 May 1995. Recorded only twice away from the interior foothills: two near TRNC 11 February–6 May 1985, and one at SJM 20 October 1994.

Acorn Woodpecker: This woodpecker is an abundant resident of oak woodlands in the interior foothills and mountains; it is a fairly common, but localized, resident of oaks in the coastal hills. The second graph refers to occasional migrants or dispersants observed in the coastal lowlands away from small, resident populations in suburban Santa Ana, where the birds use planted oaks and palms.

Yellow-bellied Sapsucker: Seven records in late fall/winter: adult male in Garden Grove 5 January 1980; adult male in lower Silverado Canyon each winter from 1980/81 to 1983/84 (earliest date 26 November 1983, latest date 18 March 1981); immature female in Santa Ana 13-17 March 1985; adult male in Newport Beach 1 February-1 March 1987; immature female in Tustin Hills 6-18 January 1988; immature female in Mission Viejo 22-31 December 1993; and an adult female at IRP 8 November 1995. An adult at DBSP 18

January-16 March 1996 showed a blending of red and white feathering on the throat, suggesting a possible Red-naped Sapsucker hybrid (not graphed).

Red-naped Sapsucker: On average, two are seen each fall/winter. One at HCP 19 September 1993 was an early migrant. Observers seem to be detecting hybrids with Red-breasted Sapsucker with increasing frequency. Hybrids with Yellow-bellied Sapsucker may also occur (see preceding species account).

Red-breasted Sapsucker: This sapsucker is an uncommon migrant and winter visitor to woodlands and landscaped areas county-wide. One at HCP 12 September 1987 was an early fall migrant.

Williamson's Sapsucker: Four winter records: Lemon Heights 28 December 1972; female at upper Silverado Canyon 18 December 1983 (SG); female in Fullerton 23 December 1984-14 March 1985; and female in Anaheim Hills 2-3 March 1990.

Nuttall's Woodpecker: Fairly common resident of woodlands in extensive natural open spaces. Small numbers of dispersing birds appear in lowland parks and isolated riparian woodlands away from breeding areas in fall and winter. Nuttall's X Downy hybrids are occasionally noted where the two species share habitat (e.g., Tonner Canyon 5 July 1988, BR during winters of 1993/94 and 1994/95).

Downy Woodpecker: This tiny woodpecker is an uncommon resident of well developed willow woodlands from the coast to the foothills, the local population apparently having increased somewhat during the past decade. Dispersing birds occur rarely in parks and lowland riparian areas where nesting is not known (e.g., TRNC, ENC, OCNC). Hybrids with Nuttall's Woodpecker are known (see preceding species account).

Hairy Woodpecker: Rare, localized resident in and around coniferous forest of the higher mountain canyons, with very few records away from such areas. Two records of birds wintering in the coastal lowlands: UNB 17 November 1987-23 February 1988, and HCP 21 September 1993-15 March 1994.

White-headed Woodpecker: Two records: inland CBC 29 December 1948, and Blue Jay Campground 14 November 1987-24 January 1988.

Northern Flicker: "Red-shafted" birds of the brownish backed, brownish headed race *C.a. collaris* nest fairly commonly in the mountains, uncommonly in the foothills, and very rarely in lowland parks and similar settings. Unitt's (1984) analysis showed that most of the flickers we see in fall and winter belong to *C.a. canescens*, an interior race not recognized by the AOU (1957) that shows slightly more gray on the back and head than *collaris*. Wintering birds are most common in parks that feature large trees and open ground.

Birds showing "Yellow-shafted" (*C.a. auritus* group) characteristics are found an average of twice per winter. These warrant careful study since apparent intergrades outnumber "pure" Yellow-shafteds (cf. Short 1971, Unitt 1984).

Olive-sided Flycatcher: Pequegnat (1951) reported nesting in UTC Big-cone Douglas-fir stands; recent observations of multiple birds in UTC (e.g., two at Yaeger Mesa 12 June 1994, one near the Main Divide 26 June 1994) suggest that nesting still occurs there sparingly.

Spring and fall migrants are uncommon in the foothills and lowlands. Two records of early spring migrants: OCNC 10 April 1981, and SRAS 6 April 1992. One at OCNC 19 July 1985 (away from apparent nesting habitat) was probably a local dispersant or extremely early fall migrant. Two records of late fall migrants: OCNC 16 October 1981, and HCP 6-9 October 1984. Two winter records, both from the Tustin Hills: 21 December 1974, and 20 December 1982-8 February 1983.

Greater Pewee: The two fall migrant records are the earliest for California: HCP 11 September 1991, and ENC 14 September 1991. Two winter records, both from the Tustin Hills: 18-21 December 1977, and 10-13 February 1991.

Western Wood-Pewee: This flycatcher breeds commonly in woodlands of the mountains, and very locally in well developed oak-riparian woodlands of the interior foothills (e.g., SRAS). Gallagher (1993) reported confirmed nesting at El Moro Canyon (San Joaquin Hills) and possible nesting elsewhere near the coast.

Transients are common in spring and fairly common in fall county-wide. One at OCNC 29 March 1988 was a very early spring migrant. A non-breeder that summered at HCP in 1995 was exceptional, being on the coastal plain. Four records of late fall migrants: HCP 20-21 October 1983; HCP 25 October 1984; HCP 22 October 1985; and an exceptionally late bird in Huntington Beach 28-29 November 1994 (several experienced observers considered this bird's plumage and calls to be consistent with Western Wood-Pewee).

Willow Flycatcher: The federally endangered "Southwestern" Willow Flycatcher (*E.t. extimus*) nested in dense willow thickets of the coastal lowlands until at least the mid-1960s (#LACM 66116, with "testes enlarged," was one of two birds taken at Capistrano Beach 8 July 1966; see Unitt 1987). Loss of the local breeding population must have resulted largely from habitat destruction, habitat fragmentation, and brood parasitism by the Brown-headed Cowbird. S&H (1979) termed Willow Flycatcher a "fairly common summer resident in riparian woodlands...of lowlands and up into canyons," but apparently mistook typically late spring migrants for breeding birds (the timing of the spring passage was given as "about April-May").

Presently, Willow Flycatchers occur only during spring and fall migration periods; most of these birds presumably belong to the northern race, *E.t. extimus*. Transients approach "uncommon" status during spring, and are only slightly more abundant during the fall passage. Early spring migrants were at TRNC 6 May 1984, and at HCP 3 May 1992. Three recent records after the second week of June ("paired" behavior not observed): two at VPB 26 June 1980; one at Seal Beach 18 June 1988; and two along SDC 18 June 1989 (RAH). One at ENC 8 August 1993 was an early fall migrant; one at HCP 12-16 November 1986 was a very late fall migrant.

Least Flycatcher: Fall migrants may be very difficult to distinguish from Dusky Flycatcher, and several such birds have been left unidentified by experienced observers. Seven record of fall migrants: HCP 8-9 October 1983; SARA 16-18 September 1986; HCP 11 November 1987; Bommer Canyon 15 September 1991; HCP 6-9 October 1991; HCP 11-16 September 1992; and Corona del Mar 5-9 November 1994. Four winter records: HCP 13 November 1981-1 March 1982; Mission Viejo 30 November 1987-13 February 1988 (end date per RH); MRP 24 December 1994-6 January 1995; and Canyon Park, Costa Mesa, 1 January-17 March 1996.

Hammond's Flycatcher: Spring migrants are uncommon, with high daily counts of five to six. Records of fall migrants average two to three per year. Two records of late fall migrants: TRNC 18 November 1987, and UTC 21 November 1993. Three winter records: ENC 5 January-11 March 1986; Craig Regional Park 26 January-23 February 1990; and El Toro 27-28 January 1995. Due to identification difficulties, one at OCNC 12 April 1980 was apparently the first county record.

Dusky Flycatcher: First recorded at HCP 25 April 1985, this confusing *Empidonax* flycatcher has since proven to be regular in spring (at least 14 records since 1990, including at least six in 1995 alone). Four fall records: HCP 20-24 October 1988; UCI 6 November 1988; HCP 12-16 September 1993; and HCP 15-17 September 1994. One winter record: Laguna Hills 14 December 1991-7 March 1992.

Gray Flycatcher: Typically, two or three spring migrants are detected each year, only very rarely before the third week of April; high seasonal totals include seven in 1991 and approximately 20 in 1995 (exceptional for the region). Two records of early spring migrants in the first week of April: TRNC 6 April 1983, and SARM 5 April 1995. Three records of late spring migrants: Capistrano Beach 24 May 1968; ENC 24 May 1980; and Gypsum Canyon 17 May 1990.

While this flycatcher is more common in spring, one to three have been found each fall since 1988, mostly during the second half of September.

Gray Flycatcher is perhaps regular in winter, with records averaging about one per year since 1980; four in 1987/88 was exceptional. Wintering birds may linger through the end of March.

Pacific-slope Flycatcher: This flycatcher nests commonly in well-developed riparian woodlands of the mountains. It breeds uncommonly to fairly commonly in the foothills and lowlands, utilizing riparian woodlands, oak woodlands, wooded parks and eucalyptus windrows (Gallagher 1993). Since the first winter record in 1984/85, "Western" Flycatchers have been recorded nine of twelve winters, with a high seasonal total of three in 1989/90.

Black Phoebe: This confiding flycatcher is a familiar sight in riparian areas and around human settlements in the lowlands, foothills, and lower mountain canyons. An influx can be perceived in fall and winter, particularly in urban and suburban neighborhoods and other marginal habitats.

Say's Phoebe: This phoebe is a rare to uncommon summer resident of grasslands and sparse shrublands from the coast to the interior foothills. Nesting substrates include cliffs, vertical streambed banks and human structures. It is a common migrant and winter visitor, occupying a range of open habitats.

Eastern Phoebe: Records average approximately one per year, with most remaining to winter. Two records of early fall migrants: Bommer Canyon 28-29 October 1987, and Westminster 11-12 October 1991. One lingered at San Clemente until 6 April 1968.

Vermilion Flycatcher: S&H (1979) called this perky flycatcher a "rare fall and winter visitor...September-February." Recorded eight times since 1979/80; six of these wintered, including three birds that have returned one or two additional winters. A female returning for its second winter at Seal Beach 7 September 1995-9 March 1996 was early.

Dusky-capped Flycatcher: One in Huntington Beach 28 November 1994 (*) was apparently a fall migrant. Four winter records: Irvine 30 December 1979-10 February 1980; Mission Viejo 21 November 1987-3 April 1988; Santa Ana 12 December 1991-4 April 1992 (*); and Mile Square Park 29 December 1994-15 January 1995 (*).

Ash-throated Flycatcher: This flycatcher nests fairly commonly in oak and sycamore riparian woodlands, primarily in the interior of the county. The first spring migrants often arrive during the last week of March; the earliest was at SORP 22 March 1984. Winter records have averaged one per year since 1983/84, with a high seasonal total of five in 1992/93. The latest known wintering bird lingered at HCP until 9 March 1985.

Great Crested Flycatcher: Two records of fall migrants: DBSP 30 September 1985, and Canyon Park in Costa Mesa 25 September 1995 (*).

Brown-crested Flycatcher: One along a tributary to Oso Creek in Mission Viejo 18 December 1993-22 January 1994 (end date per MTH) was the state's first winter record.

Sulphur-bellied Flycatcher: One at HCP 13 September 1991 was the state's earliest record of a fall migrant.

Tropical Kingbird: Fall migrant records average approximately one per year; one at PCRP 26-27 November 1993 was late. Three records of wintering birds: one in Huntington Beach three consecutive winters (18-31 December 1976, 17-28 December 1977, and 1-6 January 1979); Anaheim Lakes 13 November 1990-16 February 1991, returning 31 December 1991-29 February 1992; and Costa Mesa 2 January-6 February 1994.

Cassin's Kingbird: Nests fairly commonly, but somewhat locally, in tall trees throughout the southern lowlands and foothills; generally quite rare on the urbanized coastal plain north and west of Costa Mesa (e.g., seldom recorded at HCP). Eucalyptus stands are frequently used throughout the year. Numbers are somewhat reduced during winter, although concentrations may be found at SJM and in expansive stands of eucalyptus.

Thick-billed Kingbird: One wintered in the Tustin Hills from 1982/83 through 1991/92 (first recorded 19 December 1982; the earliest arrival date was 26 October 1985 and the latest departure date was 9 April 1983). A second bird wintered at Seal Beach 29 October 1991-25 April 1992, returning 9 October 1992-20 March 1993.

Western Kingbird: This widespread migrant nests uncommonly and locally in the coastal hills and interior foothills. One at YRP 5 March 1981 was an early spring arrival. Two records of late fall migrants: SJM 24 October-6 November 1992, and Seal Beach 18 October-1 November 1994. One in Mission Viejo 10-15 February 1982 was the second winter record for southern California.

Eastern Kingbird: Two records of spring migrants: CCSP 11-13 June 1987, and Fountain Valley 12 June 1989. Five fall records, four prior to 1970: Laguna Beach 28 August 1917; Modjeska Canyon 13 September 1958; Dana Point 15-28 September 1964; Laguna Beach 19-21 September 1969; and HCP 10 September 1986.

Scissor-tailed Flycatcher: Two fall records of adults: CCSP 6-7 August 1989, and Carbon Canyon Regional Park 23-27 October 1995. Three records of adults that may have wintered locally: UNB 17 March-27 April 1991; UNB/SJM 14 October-12 November 1991; and Laguna Beach 17-25 March 1992. S&H (1979) published a record from Anaheim in "April, 1947" (ø), but the record is considered unacceptable since details are lacking.

Horned Lark: Willett (1933) called "California" Horned Lark (*O.c. actia*) an "abundant resident from coast to base of mountains." S&H (1979) considered this a "common migrant and winter visitant [and] fairly common summer resident." Subsequent loss of the Plano Trabuco to development significantly reduced the county's nesting and wintering numbers. Horned Larks now nest fairly commonly, but quite locally, in the county's remaining shortgrass grasslands, rangelands and agricultural fields. An influx is apparent from October through February, when the species is somewhat more widespread and forms larger flocks.

Purple Martin: As summarized by S&H (1979), this cavity-dweller nested at scattered locales (e.g., Balboa, IRP, Irvine Lake) prior to arrival of competing European Starlings in the 1950s. A general scarcity of starlings in the higher mountains, however, suggests that other factors (e.g., long-term climate changes) contributed to the Purple Martin's local decline. Small numbers nested at ONRP through 1981, and at UTC through 1988. More recently, on 18 June 1995, a pair was observed collecting nesting materials at Oso Reservoir. Since 1980, spring migrants have been recorded away from potential breeding habitat six times (26 March to 14 May); fall migrants have been recorded twice: HCP 8 September 1984, and SARM 24 July 1993.

Tree Swallow: During recent years, small numbers have summered at scattered locales including SDC, VPB and some reservoirs; nesting has been confirmed at SJM and PCRP. This swallow is locally common fall through spring at SJM; elsewhere in the lowlands and foothills it is a common spring migrant, uncommon to fairly common fall migrant, and rare winter visitor.

Violet-green Swallow: This attractive swallow breeds fairly commonly, but quite locally, in the foothills and mountains. Spring transients are fairly common in March and April, and fall transients are uncommon from early September to early October, occurring primarily at inland reservoirs. Along the coast, transients are rare to uncommon at SJM (e.g., 25 on 16 October 1994 was exceptional, particularly for fall) and are very rare elsewhere (e.g., only two records from HCP). Two summer records from coastal areas: San Clemente 10 June 1959 (#WFVZ 43074), and TRNC 6 June-18 July 1984. As a measure of its winter status, Violet-green Swallow has been recorded on 12 inland and six coastal CBCs since 1961, with a high count of 20 on the 1980 inland count.

Northern Rough-winged Swallow: This swallow is a fairly common to common migrant and summer resident in the lowlands and foothills; it nests in small to moderate colonies along streambeds, often utilizing bridges. Spring migrants typically arrive in mid-February; six at SJM 22 January 1995 appeared to be early migrants. One to three have wintered at SJM most years since 1984/85, with occasional sightings elsewhere.

Bank Swallow: Historically, this swallow was known to nest at Huntington Beach, Newport Beach and SJC (Shepardson 1909, Willett 1912, Burnham et al. 1917, Pequegnat 1951). Oddly, it was unrecorded between the 1960s and 14 May 1984, when one was seen at TRNC. Subsequently, records have averaged approximately two each spring and four each fall. Two records of apparent early spring migrants: IRP 28 February 1990, and YRP 3 March 1990. One at DBSP 2 July 1989 was unseasonal. Two records of early fall migrants: UNB 21 July 1986, and SJM 6-13 August 1994. One winter record: SJM 2 January-19 February 1994.

Cliff Swallow: The most common, widespread swallow from early spring through late summer. A group of 20 at SJM 11 February 1995 was exceptional for early spring. Late fall migrants were at HCP 5 October 1986 and SBNWR 24 October 1991. One acceptable winter record: SJM 31 December 1993-30 January 1994, and what is taken to be the same individual there 22 January 1995. An unsubstantiated report of 20 on the 1964 coastal CBC (S&H 1979) is presumably erroneous.

Barn Swallow: This swallow nests fairly commonly to commonly at coastal sites near water, and seems to be increasing inland (e.g., 17 adults and young near SORP 7 July 1995). The first birds typically arrive in late February. Four records of apparent early spring migrants: four at HCP 4 February 1989; three at SARA 4 February 1989; one or two at SJM 5 February 1989; and three at SJM 30 January 1993. Since 1984/85, wintering Barn Swallows have been nearly regular at SJM (occasionally occurring elsewhere), with a high count of three or four there 2 December 1990.

Steller's Jay: Three acceptable records: two on the inland CBC 29 December1963; one at ONRP 28 December 1973 (inland CBC); and one in Garden Grove 15 March 1974. One at OCNC 24 June 1986 and other occasional unseasonal reports probably pertain to birds released from captivity.

Western Scrub-Jay: Abundant resident of native upland communities throughout most of the county, also occupying urban parks and other areas with well developed landscaping. This scrub-jay is generally quite scarce on the coastal plain west of the Santa Ana River and south of Westminster. Formerly known as the Scrub Jay.

Clark's Nutcracker: Four were recorded on the inland CBC 30 December 1961, with "other records this month" (*Audubon Field Notes* 16:285). This was during a winter when the species was found at relatively low elevations throughout much of the state.

American Crow: This opportunistic corvid is most abundant in areas altered by human activities. In District 3, the species occurs only very locally in relatively open portions of the southern Santa Ana Mountains where human presence is conspicuous (e.g., BJC and El Cariso Station [Riverside County]). For example, DRW observed "many" at BJC 14 November 1987 and RAH observed 15 at BJC 25 June 1994.

Common Raven: Pequegnat (1951) considered this corvid to be an "uncommon resident" of the mountains, with "only a few pairs [inhabiting] the northern portions of the range in vicinity of Sierra Peak." Apparently benefitting from large-scale human modifications to the landscape, the species is now common in the foothills and fairly common in the mountains; as many as 1000 roost nightly at IRP outside of the nesting season. Common Ravens are rare on the coastal plain northwest of Huntington Beach.

Mountain Chickadee: A limited population occupies coniferous forests of the Santa Ana Mountains; daily counts seldom exceed 20. Small numbers are reported almost every fall/winter in the interior foothills; an exceptional concentration of at least 25 was at ONRP 17 December 1989. Although normally quite rare in the lowlands, chickadees were recorded at "numerous locations" near the coast in 1987-88; two in Westminster 29 August were the earliest.

Plain Titmouse: In the Santa Ana Mountains, Pequegnat (1951) considered this an "abundant resident [from] 1000 to 4500 feet; in winter found extensively in chaparral as high as Santiago Peak, [withdrawing] to base of mountain during unusually cold periods." We consider Plain Titmouse to be a common resident of oak woodlands in the mountains and adjacent foothills, and a generally uncommon resident of oaks in the San Joaquin Hills. Wanderers are rarely encountered elsewhere (e.g., YRP 21 January-15 February 1993, and again there 11 February 1995).

Bushtit: This familiar bird is an abundant, widespread resident of shrublands, woodlands and landscaped areas. Observers typically encounter pairs in spring, family groups and small flocks in summer, and flocks of 20 to 60 or more in fall and winter.

Red-breasted Nuthatch: This nuthatch prefers large conifers, but may be found in a range of trees, including eucalyptus and oaks. During periodic "irruption" years, it is typically uncommon in the lowlands and fairly common in the higher mountains. During non-irruption years, the species is normally absent, or virtually absent, from the foothills and lowlands, although small numbers may occur in the higher mountains. An early fall migrant was at UTC 18 August 1984, and one to four were present there 26 August-20 September 1995.

White-breasted Nuthatch: This nuthatch is a fairly common resident of oaks in the foothills and mountains. It is normally very rare elsewhere, although lowland reports were widespread winter of 1987-1988, with two at HCP 9 August being the earliest and a high count of six at HCP 1 September.

Pygmy Nuthatch: Small numbers from outside the county invade conifers from the coast to the mountains during infrequent "irruption" years; high counts include eight in Lemon Heights 6-9 November 1987, and five or six at UTC 30 January-6 February 1993. Pequegnat (1951) considered this a "rare resident [of] Coulter Pines Forest in Horsethief Canyon district [Riverside County?], in March, June, and October; elevation 4100 feet."

Brown Creeper:. Recorded most years, with a high seasonal total of six during winter 1986/87. This inconspicuous bird may be a regular migrant and/or winter visitor in the mountains, but most records are from the coastal lowlands, where observer coverage is far better.

Cactus Wren: This large wren is a fairly common resident of coastal sage scrub containing significant cactus patches in the coastal hills and foothills. Wanderers are occasionally noted away from resident populations, exceptionally in areas that lack cactus (e.g., BC 14 November 1983, SARA 11-15 August 1992).

Rock Wren: Due to a general lack of open, rocky areas, this is one of the county's scarcest nesting birds (Gallagher 1993); minor concentrations are known from the Chino Hills, northern Santa Ana Mountains and Shady Canyon in the northern San Joaquin Hills. A weak influx in fall and winter is mostly evident in parts of the coastal lowlands where the species is not known to breed (e.g., records from UNB, BC, SARM, Dana Point).

Canyon Wren: Uncommon, local resident of steep, remote areas. Relatively accessible locations include Aliso and Wood Canyons Regional Park and Caspers Wilderness Park.

Bewick's Wren: Rare away from native plant communities and dense plantings near natural open spaces (e.g., few records from HCP); a pair presently breeds at ENC. Unlike the following species, Bewick's Wren does not widely withdraw from the foothills and mountains during the colder months.

House Wren: This vociferous wren breeds abundantly in riparian and oak woodlands of the mountains and foothills. In the lowlands, loss of woodlands to development has reduced the overall breeding status to fairly common along streams and in adjacent uplands. After raising young, most birds withdraw from the interior foothills and mountains, and the species becomes uncommon to fairly common in dense ornamental plantings of the lowlands. These seasonal shifts in status and habitat usage probably involve a significant influx of birds from outside the local area.

Winter Wren: Fall/winter records average approximately one per year. Perhaps due to this wren's secretive habits and the county's general lack of dense, moist thickets attractive to this species, there are only two records that extend over two weeks (including one that wintered at UCI in 1984/85 and 1985/86).

Sedge Wren: One at HCP 15-17 October 1991 provided the fourth California record, and the first in the state south of San Francisco.

Marsh Wren: The sedentary *C.p. clarkae*, recently described by Unitt et al. (1996), breeds commonly at UNB and SJM (and probably SBNWR); the remainder of the local breeding range is incompletely known. In the interior, nesting was known at the Anaheim Wetlands (SARA) until 1996, when habitat conditions apparently became unsuitable for this species. Marsh Wrens are more common and widespread during fall and winter due to a significant influx of migratory subspecies that breed outside the county.

American Dipper: Recorded once in winter: upper SJC 27 January 1988.

Golden-crowned Kinglet: This colorful bird is a rare, regular winter visitor to conifers of the mountains. In the foothills and lowlands, fall migrants are nearly annual; wintering birds occur primarily during periodic "irruption" years. As this species was unrecorded by Pequegnat (1951), the first record may have been a male collected at UTC 20 October 1960 (#CSULB 2425).

Ruby-crowned Kinglet: This is a common, widespread migrant and winter visitor from the coast to the mountains. Three records of late spring migrants, all in 1995: HCP 16-20 May; two at HCP 21 May; and Costa Mesa 21 May. Two at HCP 5 September 1987 were early fall migrants.

Blue-gray Gnatcatcher: This small insectivore nests fairly commonly, but locally, in mixed live oak/chaparral habitat of the mountains. The graph estimates the timing of movements in District 3. Blue-gray Gnatcatchers nest rarely and locally in the foothills, at least during non-drought periods (e.g., DRW observed two pairs nest-building at WRP 26 April and 10 May 1995, with an additional territorial male present on the second date). The presence of up to three birds in maritime chaparral habitat in Laguna Niguel 18 March-30 May 1991, with one observed 19 July 1991, suggests that a small nesting population exists in this coastal area, as well.

In the coastal lowlands, Blue-gray Gnatcatcher is primarily a fairly common migrant and uncommon winter visitor. One at HCP 8 May 1994 was a late spring migrant. Two at HCP 4 August 1990 were early fall migrants or dispersing birds.

California Gnatcatcher: Vegetation, slope and elevation greatly affect the status and distribution of the federally threatened "Coastal" California Gnatcatcher (*P.c. californica*). Nesting occurs primarily in coastal sage scrub and coastal bluff scrub communities, and locally in chaparral, mulefat scrub and saltbush scrub communities. California Sagebrush (*Artemisia californica*),

California Sunflower (*Encelia californica*) and California Buckwheat (*Eriogonum fasciculatum*) are especially favored for nesting; associations dominated by Black Sage (*Salvia mellifera*) tend to be used only sparingly. Foraging adults are occasionally noted in adjacent communities, including scrub/grassland ecotones.

In proper habitat, California Gnatcatchers are uncommon to fairly common on gentle to moderate slopes on the immediate coast, in the Fullerton Hills, on the coastal slope of Loma Ridge, and in the southern foothills; they are absent to uncommon on moderate to steep slopes below approximately 800 feet elevation, and are generally scarce above this elevation. An exception to this rule is found at SRAS, where surveys conducted for the County of Orange in 1992 yielded eleven pairs between 1000 and 1620 feet.

Outside of the nesting season, dispersing and foraging birds regularly use weedy areas and other non-scrub habitats in the general vicinity of occupied scrub. Exotic landscaping is avoided at all times. Two records in sparse scrub surrounding the BC wetlands (two on 10 September 1988, and one on 25 April 1993) probably pertained to dispersants from SARM. As a measure of the recent increase in our understanding of the California Gnatcatcher, S&H (1979 p. 20) suggested that the species might have been extirpated from the county.

Western Bluebird: Fairly common, but localized, breeder in the county's interior; rare on the coastal plain. Pequegnat (1951) considered this bluebird "common" (presumably refering mainly to foothill sites), and S&H (1979) called it "fairly common in foothills and lower portions of canyons." The status declined to "uncommon" during the 1980s, presumably due to competition with European Starlings for natural cavity nesting sites, but provision of nest boxes by RLP and others at IRP, YRP, ONRP and other sites has yielded exciting results. In the higher mountains, open oak woodlands around BJC are occupied, and observations of family groups and small flocks at UTC throughout the year suggest nesting there, as well.

Mountain Bluebird: Typically absent or very scarce except during periodic "irruption" years when this bluebird may be locally common (e.g., up to 175 in the San Joaquin Hills fall/winter 1993-94). A flock of approximately 60 in Shady Canyon (northern San Joaquin Hills) during winter 1994/95 was unusual since the species was otherwise unrecorded during that season. One at Signal Peak 28-29 March 1993 was late and was not part of a local or regional "irruption."

Townsend's Solitaire: Pequegnat (1951) considered this a "commona (sic) winter visitant in woodland belt around 4000 feet." S&H (1979) termed it an "uncommon winter visitor." Townsend's Solitaire presently winters only in small numbers in the higher mountains; a recent high count was ten on the inland CBC, 17 December 1994. Four records away from the mountains: Laguna Beach 31 May 1987 (very late); Bommer Canyon 4 November 1987; Laguna Canyon 12-18 March 1992; and HCP 18 April 1992.

Swainson's Thrush: S&H (1979) considered this thrush a "fairly common summer resident in willows, alders in moist canyons of foothills and mountains (up to 3000 feet in Trabuco Canyon)." The local nesting population has undoubtedly declined greatly compared with historic times, due to habitat loss, habitat degradation and/or cowbird parasitism; breeders now occur rarely and very locally in dense riparian thickets of the San Joaquin Hills, foothills and mountains, with evidence of continued decline in just the past few years.

Swainson's Thrush is a fairly common spring migrant and uncommon fall migrant county-wide; 100 at HCP 20 May 1989 (DRW) was a very high estimated daily count. One at TRNC 9 April 1986 was an early spring migrant. The earliest fall migrant was at TRNC 25 August 1986. Four records of late fall migrants: Caspers Wilderness Park 30 October-1 November 1981; ENC 8 November 1981; ENC 17 October 1985; and SJM 21 October 1995.

Hermit Thrush: Based on Unitt's (1984) analysis, most migrants and wintering birds are of the warm brown races *C.g. guttatus* and *C.g. nanus* that breed in Alaska and British Columbia. Paler, gray-backed birds belonging to *C.g. slevini*, *C.g. sequoiensis* and/or *C.g. auduboni* may be regular in April; the only fall record of a gray-backed bird, UTC 20 September 1995, represents the earliest Hermit Thrush arrival on record. Of five mid-May records from the lowlands, only one at ENC 21 May 1995 is known to represent a gray-backed bird.

Hermit Thrushes, presumably *C.g. sequoiensis*, formerly nested at UTC and possibly other mountain canyons. Pequegnat (1951) heard the song at UTC on 12 June 1941 and 15 June 1944, and a juvenal male was taken at "Trabuco Canyon, upper camp" 26 July 1958 (#CSULB 2483). S&H (1979) heard two or three singing "in the big-cone Douglas-Fir grove above Yaeger Mesa" (UTC) until 10 June 1974. Recent directed searches by RAH in UTC and other likely canyons have not yielded evidence of continued nesting.

Rufous-backed Robin: Two overlapping records: one at ENC 1 January 1983, joined by a second 23 February 1983 through 5 March (date span per CBRC), with one remaining to 11 April.

American Robin: First noted breeding in north Irvine in 1982, this personable bird is now a fairly common, localized breeder in well vegetated parks and similar settings. A variable influx is noted in fall/winter, when the status fluctuates between fairly common and common.

Varied Thrush: Pequegnat (1951) considered this thrush "common" in winter, while S&H (1979) considered it an "irregular, uncommon migrant and winter visitor." Varied Thrush is now generally rare and possibly regular in winter, approaching "uncommon" status only in oak woodlands of the foothills and mountains during infrequent "flight years." Early fall migrants were at HCP 8 October 1988 and TRNC 2 October 1989.

Wrentit: This small, vocal bird is among the most abundant residents of intact coastal sage scrub and chaparral communities. Considering this species' general reluctance to utilize non-native vegetation, or to sustain flight for even moderate distances, it is not surprising that Wrentits are often absent from isolated fragments of otherwise suitable habitat.

Gray Catbird: Two records of fall migrants: SARM 19 October 1990, and HCP 12-31 October 1992. One record of a wintering bird at Canyon Park, Costa Mesa, 31 December 1995-19 February 1996.

Northern Mockingbird: This flashy songster is a familiar fixture in residential neighborhoods county-wide. It is fairly common (locally common) in coastal sage scrub, alluvial scrub, and broken chaparral of the lowlands and foothills.

Sage Thrasher: Three records of apparent spring migrants: Buena Park 1 March 1925; UNB 24 March 1990; and UCI 18 February 1994. Two records of fall migrants: SJM 9 September 1990, and SBNWR 24 November 1995. Four winter (or early spring) records: Garden Grove 6 February 1971; Laguna Hills 9-17 December 1989; SJM 24 December 1990; and IRP 2 February 1991.

Brown Thrasher: One spring record: Laguna Beach 7-8 May 1993. Three fall records: ENC 27 November 1980; HCP 23 October 1988; and Huntington Beach 7-9 November 1990. Two winter records: Huntington Beach 10 January-7 March 1987, and MRP 11 December 1988-18 February 1989. S&H (1979) published a report of two on the 1951 inland CBC, but this record is unacceptable due to a lack of details.

Bendire's Thrasher: Three fall records: TRNC 21 July 1985 (early); HCP 11 October 1992; and SARM 2 October 1993. Individuals at SJM and Mile Square Park were adequately documented on the 30 December 1979 coastal CBC; these birds probably wintered locally.

California Thrasher: Common but visually inconspicuous resident of chaparral-covered slopes in the higher mountains; best located by voice in early spring. California Thrashers are fairly common in extensive blocks of chaparral and coastal sage scrub in the lowlands and foothills, occasionally utilizing adjacent landscaped areas. One in coastal bluff scrub vegetation at

SARM 17 March 1992 was either a wanderer or "last survivor" of a former population there. One at HCP 4-6 March 1993 was unexpected, being well away from any extant population.

Yellow Wagtail: An immature at SJM 19-20 September 1992 was the southernmost for California.

Black-backed Wagtail: A wintering immature bird widely observed at DBSP and elsewhere along lower SJC 25 January-12 April 1996 (*) was the southernmost recorded in California. The CBRC rejected a report of a White/Black-backed Wagtail at SJM 27 October 1985 (bird seen and heard in flight).

Red-throated Pipit: Three fall records of immatures: one in an east Irvine agricultural field 9-23 October 1993, joined by a second 22 October 1993; and one in an east Irvine agricultural field 9-10 November 1995 (late).

American Pipit: Flocks of up to several hundred winter in agricultural fields and expanses of irrigated turf.. Individuals in Irvine agricultural fields 25 October 1991 (RAE) and 12 November 1995 (JEP) showed marks suggesting the Eurasian subspecies, *A.r. japonicus*, but the sightings were inconclusive.

Sprague's Pipit: One wintered at PT 2 December 1989-19 February 1990.

Bohemian Waxwing: One acceptable record: San Juan Capistrano 11 February 1969. S&H (1979) questioned two previous reports.

Cedar Waxwing: This attractive bird winters uncommonly to abundantly county-wide, favoring ornamental plantings and native vegetation that produce berries. An influx of transients is frequently evident during April and May; the increased numbers are most evident during "off" years, when local wintering flocks can be scarce. Four records of early fall migrants: one at HCP 31 August 1986; two at SJM 6 September 1995; one at HCP 9 September 1995; and one in Westminster 9 September 1995.

Nesting was suspected for a pair summering at DBSP in 1964, and confirmed there in 1965 when an adult was observed with three fledglings on 7 July (Pugh 1966). This remains the sole confirmed nesting record for coastal southern California. One other summer record: VPB 29 July 1980.

Phainopepla: Numbers of this striking bird vary from year to year. It is a fairly common to common breeder in and around woodlands of the interior foothills and mountains, and is generally uncommon in the coastal hills. Small numbers regularly winter in the interior foothills. As a measure of its winter distribution, the Phainopepla has been recorded on 37 inland CBCs versus one coastal CBC since 1946. Migrants/dispersants are occasionally found away from native habitats, primarily in May and September.

Loggerhead Shrike: This small raptor occupies relatively flat, open country, often nesting in dense vegetation near habitat edges. Loggerhead Shrikes are fairly common where suitable habitat remains in the coastal lowlands, and are generally uncommon in the county's interior. Numbers increase during the winter months, and fluctuate from year to year, but both coastal and inland CBCs show declining trends from the 1970s to the present.

White-eyed Vireo: Five records of spring migrants: HCP 21-28 May 1985; UNB 10 May 1992; SJC 26-27 June 1992; Huntington Beach 8 May 1993 (*); and HCP 31 May-1 June 1993 (*).

Bell's Vireo: Historically, "Least" Bell's Vireo (*V.b. pusillus*) was a common and widespread summer resident in well developed riparian areas throughout coastal southern California, including Orange County (e.g., Pequegnat 1951). S&H (1979) considered it a very rare migrant last known to nest at Peters Canyon in 1948.

Protection and expansion of key riparian habitat areas and intensive management actions in San Diego and Riverside counties (including control of Brown-headed Cowbirds, which parasitize vireo nests) have led to substantial regional population increases during the 1980s and 1990s, including recurrence of breeding in Orange County. The first recent nesting records were at BR and MRP in 1991; pairs or family groups have subsequently been found at scattered locales, including SDC, PCRP, VPB, SJM and SJC. Continued expansion and management of strategic riparian habitat areas should lead to further increases in the county's nesting population.

The earliest spring record of Bell's Vireo was a singing male on lower SDC 15 March 1995. A late fall migrant was in Huntington Beach 4 October 1995. Three winter records: HCP 7 September 1985-22 March 1986; MRP 14 October 1993-26 February 1994; and Corona del Mar 16 December 1993-30 January 1994.

Two fall records of birds with plumage suggesting one of the more colorful eastern races, *V.b. bellii* or *V.b. medius*: Huntington Beach 21 September 1992, and HCP 28 October 1995. Subspecific identification is best left to birds in the hand, as even the generally drab *V.b. arizonae* may show fairly bright greenish tones (SAL pers. comm.).

Solitary Vireo: "Cassin's" Solitary Vireo (*V.s. cassinii*) probably nested in the mountains earlier in the century; Pequegnat (1951) called it an "occasional summer visitant...in canyons about 2500 feet" but provided no details regarding breeding status. S&H (1979) called it an "uncommon summer resident in riparian woodland or conifers in upper parts of canyons (e.g., fairly common around Yaeger Mesa in UTC)," but apparently did not confirm breeding. WDG observed singing males at Chiquito Basin in the southern Santa Ana Mountains during successive years: two on 26 May 1987, and one on 31 May 1988. RAH did not find nesting evidence during several days of mountain field work during spring and summer 1994, although a singing male was at Bear Springs (a few hundred yards into Riverside County) 29-30 May 1994.

The first spring migrant *cassinii* often arrive during the last week of March; one at HCP 8 March 1983 may have wintered locally. Two records of early fall migrants: HCP 13-14 August 1994, and HCP 19-20 August 1995. An average of one is detected each winter, and birds have remained as late as mid-March.

"Plumbeous" Solitary Vireo (*V.s. plumbeus*) is increasingly detected as a fall migrant (high total of seven in fall 1993) and winter visitor (at least one per winter since 1987/88, with a high total of four in 1992/93); wintering birds have lingered as late as 25 April (at HCP in 1993). Two records of apparent spring migrants at HCP: 21 April 1990, and 9 June 1993 (extremely late).

"Blue-headed" Solitary Vireos (presumably *V.s. solitarius*) have been recorded eight times in fall: HCP 4-6 October 1984; TRNC 18 September 1989; HCP 20 September-4 October 1989; HCP 22 September 1990; HCP 22-28 September 1990; Costa Mesa 15 October 1992; Newport Beach 28 September 1994; and HCP 9 October 1995.

Yellow-throated Vireo: Seven records of spring migrants: TRNC 19 May 1982; HCP 25-27 May 1985; Gypsum Canyon 17 May 1990; Orange 9 May 1992; HCP 28-30 May 1992; HCP 23 May 1993 (*); and Laguna Lakes 27 May 1995 (*). Three fall records: Newport Beach 23 September 1984; HCP 26-28 September 1985; and HCP 23 October-1 November 1986. One near UNB 4 January 1988 either wintered locally or was a very late fall migrant. Orange County's 11 records exceed the total for any other California county.

Hutton's Vireo: This unassuming resident is found fairly commonly in oak woodlands throughout, and uncommonly in riparian woodlands of the foothills and mountains. It is a rare, localized resident of lowland willow woodlands (e.g., those at SARM and MRP). From August throught May, dispersing Hutton's Vireos are reported with some regularity in well vege-tated city parks and similar areas; one to two pairs have nested irregularly at HCP since 1990.

Warbling Vireo: Breeds fairly commonly in maple and alder woodlands of the mountains, and rarely in areas where these trees extend into the interior foothills (e.g., SRAS, AT, SJC). This vireo almost certainly nested in the coastal lowlands historically, before widespread loss and degradation of riparian woodlands and expansion of the local cowbird population.

Warbling Vireo is now a common spring and fall migrant county-wide, with a high daily count of approximately 120 at HCP 20 May 1995 (JEP). Two records of apparent late fall migrants: HCP 21 December 1985, and Westminster 24 November 1993. A wintering individual in Irvine Irvine 9 January-1 March 1982 was re-found 30 January 1983.

Philadelphia Vireo: Five fall/early winter records: HCP 26 November 1982-1 January 1983; HCP 5-6 October 1988; HCP 15-16 October 1989; HCP 11-14 October 1993 (*); and Irvine 30 September 1995 (*).

Red-eyed Vireo: One record of a spring migrant: OCNC 18 June 1981. One at TRNC 25 July-6 August 1985 probably summered locally. Eight records of fall migrants: HCP 11 November 1982; HCP 5 October 1988; HCP 20 October 1991; HCP 28 August-5 September 1992; SARM 4 September 1992; HCP 4-5 October 1992; Westminster 30 September-2 October 1994; and HCP 22-23 October 1994.

Yellow-green Vireo: Three acceptable records of fall migrants: Dana Point 22-27 September 1964; UCI 1 October 1988; and Costa Mesa 18 October 1990. S&H (1979) published a record from Costa Mesa 3 October 1967 (ø), but the record is considered unacceptable since details are lacking.

Blue-winged Warbler: One record of a singing male spring vagrant at HCP 28 May 1990.

Golden-winged Warbler: Four records of fall migrants: Fullerton 24 October 1982 (female); Newport Beach 30 September-1 October 1988 (male); TRNC 26-30 October 1988 (male); and Huntington Beach 19 October 1995 (male). A male at Whiting Regional Park 19 February-29 March 1992 was one of very few U.S. winter records.

Tennessee Warbler: This "eastern" warbler seems to be occurring more regularly during spring migration, with 13 records since 1989 (two previous spring records). On average, two are seen each fall; seven in fall 1989 was exceptional. One in Westminster 25-30 August 1990 was early. Six winter records, the latest lingering at HCP until 20 April 1985.

Orange-crowned Warbler: Four races should occur in the county, but most individuals are not reliably separated in the field. Collection of specimens would be useful in clarifying this species' complex status locally and elsewhere in southern California. All races winter primarily in the lowlands.

The relatively bright *V.c. lutescens* nests in canyons with riparian thickets and dense chaparral throughout much of the county.

V.c. sordida is a dull, large-billed race that nests on the Channel Islands, the Palos Verdes Peninsula and, apparently, portions of San Diego County

(G&D 1981, Unitt 1984). *Sordida* appears to be a fairly common migrant and winter visitor, and probably nests sparingly near the coast (e.g., sight records from HCP, Laguna Beach, Canyon Park in Costa Mesa).

Gray-headed birds believed to represent *V.c. orestera* and *V.c. celata* are uncommon fall migrants (arriving in early September), rare in winter.

Nashville Warbler: Spring migrants are fairly common along the coast and uncommon in the foothills. The first birds typically arrive during the last week of March or first week of April; an apparent early migrant was in a tributary to Laguna Canyon 20 March 1993 (RAH, RAE, SGM). Fall migrants are uncommon throughout the lowlands and foothills; one at TRNC 6-9 August 1984 was slightly early. Winter records average one or two per winter; at least six in 1994/95 was a high seasonal total.

Little is known about the occurrence of Nashville Warbler in the mountains. It was unrecorded by Pequegnat (1951), and a total of seven at UTC 18 August 1984 (DRW, BED, LRH) is one of few records. The graph represents our best estimate of the montane status.

Virginia's Warbler: An apparent spring migrant was at Capistrano Beach 25 April 1968. Records of fall migrants average two to three per year. An early fall migrant was in Westminster 15 August 1992. Three records of late fall migrants: Capistrano Beach 8 November 1980; ENC 9 September-27 December 1981; and Westminster 27-28 October 1990. One at ENC 19 April 1980 probably wintered locally, since one wintered there each year from 1980/81 to 1983/84 (earliest arrival date 4 September 1982, latest departure date 19 April 1980).

Lucy's Warbler: Records of fall migrants average approximately one per year, with two early records: TRNC 4 August 1984, and SJM 7 August 1993. Three late fall records, some of which may pertain to birds that wintered locally: Dana Point 15 December 1984; HCP 19 November 1987; and Mission Viejo 9-17 December 1989. Four definite winter records: Costa Mesa 11-31 January 1968; Irvine 25 February-8 March 1984; Corona del Mar 3 January-16 February 1987; and CSUF 10 December 1995-17 February 1996.

Northern Parula: Spring records generally average about one per year, excluding a remarkable total of 13 or 14 found during an unprecedented statewide influx in spring 1992. Five fall records: TRNC 22 October 1986; Seal Beach 4-12 October 1988; HCP 7 October 1992; HCP 10 December 1993 (late); and Costa Mesa 29 September 1994. One winter record of a male at YRP 19-26 March 1995.

Yellow Warbler: The "California" Yellow Warbler (*D.p. morcomi*) is a fairly common, localized breeder in dense alder and maple woodlands of the mountains (e.g., UTC, SC). Pequegnat (1951) called it an "abundant summer visitor" in the mountains, mentioning that a "cowbird from nest by warbler attracted attention to [the nest's] location."

Before expansion of local and regional cowbird populations, and widespread loss and degradation of riparian woodlands, Yellow Warblers almost certainly nested more commonly in the foothills and lowlands (cf. G&M 1944). Small numbers are found each summer in willow woodlands away from the coast, and it seems likely that a few pairs still nest in such areas.

Spring migrants are fairly common in general, and are locally common at HCP; approximately 150 there 13 May 1994 (LRH) was a very high daily count. The earliest apparent spring migrant was at SJM 5 April 1981. Fall migrants are common near the coast, uncommon in the foothills and mountains. Winter records average approximately three to four per year.

Chestnut-sided Warbler: Two records of spring migrants: ENC 16 May 1992 (male), and HCP 4 June 1990 (singing male). A singing male at TRNC 29 June-22 August 1988 was the first summer record for southern California. Fall records average approximately one per year; five or six in fall 1995 was exceptional. One at HCP 3-5 September 1994 was early; one at HCP 16-24 November 1983 was late. Five records of wintering birds or very late fall migrants: SARM 21 December 1983-3 April 1984; IRP 24 November 1991-29 February 1992; Irvine 19-28 December 1993; Huntington Beach 1 January-20 April 1996; and DBSP 6 January 1996.

Magnolia Warbler: One spring record of a singing male at HCP 3-4 June 1993. Fall records average approximately one per year.

Cape May Warbler: An immature male fall migrant was at HCP 5 September 1992. An immature female wintered in Costa Mesa 9 February-18 April 1991.

Black-throated Blue Warbler: One spring record of a singing male in Irvine 12 June 1989. Eleven acceptable records of fall migrants, ten since 1985, including an extremely late female at HCP 27-28 December 1989. A male wintered in Placentia 16 December 1986 to "late February" 1987.

Yellow-rumped Warbler: "Audubon's Warbler" (*D.c. auduboni* group) is among the county's most abundant and widespread winter visitors. One at HCP 3 June 1991 was a late spring migrant. Early fall migrants were at TRNC 6 September 1984, and at YRP 5-10 September 1995.

"Myrtle Warbler" (*D.c. coronata* group) is uncommon, occurring primarily in well vegetated parks and riparian areas.

Black-throated Gray Warbler: This warbler probably nested in the county historically. Pequegnat (1951) confusingly termed it an "occasional summer visitant to the woodland vegetation as high as 4500 feet. Common from May 3 to October 1, but only occasional specimens are encountered in vicinity of springs during May and June." S&H (1979) called it a "fairly common summer resident, locally, in live oaks and conifers in mountains (e.g., Trabuco Canyon)." RAH did not find nesting evidence during several days of mountain field work in spring and summer 1994, but found a singing male at Bear Springs (a few hundred yards into Riverside County) 29-30 May 1994. One in chaparral (away from potential nesting habitat) along the Main Divide in the southern Santa Ana Mountains 18 June 1994 may have summered locally.

Black-throated Gray Warbler is now a fairly common spring and fall transient that can be locally common at concentration points like HCP. The first spring migrants typically arrive during the last week of March. One at HCP 9 June 1993 was a late spring migrant in the coastal lowlands. An average of four or five winter in the lowlands and foothills each year, with a high seasonal total of approximately 15 in winter 1989/90. One at SC (approximately 3000 feet elevation) 21 January 1993 provided the lone winter record from the Santa Ana Mountains.

Townsend's Warbler: This warbler is a fairly common transient throughout, mid-April through mid-May and early September through mid-October. Approximately 80 at HCP 13 May 1994 (LRH) was a very high count. One at TRNC 5 June 1989 was a late spring migrant. One at HCP 4 August 1990 was an early fall migrant. Wintering birds are uncommon along the coast, rare inland. Five spring records of Townsend's X Hermit hybrids: HCP 3 May 1985; TRNC 3 May 1989; ENC 21 April 1990; OCNC 30 April 1990; and HCP 1 May 1994.

Hermit Warbler: This warbler is an uncommon spring migrant, with high daily counts of 12 recorded twice at HCP: 30 April 1989 (LRH), and 20 May 1995 (JEP). Late spring migrants were found at Laguna Beach 7 June 1992 and HCP 3 June 1995. Numbers are reduced in fall, although counts of seven or eight in the Santa Ana Mountains 18 August 1984 and three at UTC 20 September 1995 suggest a moderate montane passage. Approximately eight winter records, five since 1990/91.

Pequegnat (1951) considered it "highly probable that a few birds breed" in the Santa Ana Mountains, reporting one record from Bear Springs (Riverside County) on 13 June of an unidentified year. This assessment was inconsistent with the species' known breeding range at that time (cf. G&M 1944).

Black-throated Green Warbler: Eleven records of fall migrants, all since 1982. Two winter records of females: HCP 12 November 1982-4 February 1983, and SARM 2 December 1983-6 April 1984.

Blackburnian Warbler: Twelve fall records, eleven since 1984.

Grace's Warbler: One record of a wintering bird at Newport Beach 21 February-29 March 1987 (end date per JLD), presumably returning to the same location 22 November 1987 (ø; this private area was not thoroughly covered thereafter).

Pine Warbler: Two winter records: YRP 14 January-2 April 1989 (male), and Laguna Beach 24 November 1991-15 March 1992 (immature female).

Prairie Warbler: Nine records of fall migrants, eight since 1987 and four in 1991 alone; individuals at HCP 4-5 September 1989 and 31 August-7 September 1992 were early.

Palm Warbler: Five records of apparent or possible spring migrants: HCP 14 April 1982; Huntington Beach 3-5 April 1989; HCP 3 May 1990; Laguna Beach 6 April 1994; and Huntington Beach 5-6 April 1995. Records of fall migrants average three or four per year, with an exceptional seasonal total of 11-12 in 1993. Early fall migrants were at SARA 21 September 1984 and Irvine 18 September 1995. Winter records average nearly two per year, with a high seasonal total of eight in 1987/88. The latest wintering Palm Warbler lingered at DBSP until 3 May 1985.

Bay-breasted Warbler: A singing male at OCNC 1 June 1984 is one of very few spring records for coastal southern California. Three fall records of immatures: DBSP 29 September-11 October 1981; HCP 12-25 October 1987; and HCP 21-22 September 1990.

Blackpoll Warbler: Two exceptional spring records, both singing males: TRNC 13 June 1988, and HCP 8 July 1995 (late). Records of fall migrants average approximately five per year, with a high seasonal total of ten or 11 in 1987; the vast majority occur within a few miles of the coast. Four records of late fall migrants: Mission Viejo 14 November 1985; a lingering bird at HCP until 7 November 1993; Huntington Beach 12 November 1994; and a sick bird at IRP 29 October-11 November 1995.

Cerulean Warbler: An immature male was at UCI 1-3 October 1988.

Black-and-white Warbler: Records of spring migrants average approximately two per year, the birds arriving as early as the last week of April; two late records: BR 25-27 June 1993, and VPB 26 June 1993. Fall migrant records average approximately four per year; one at TRNC 10 August 1987 was early. Since 1988/89, winter records have averaged one to two per year.

American Redstart: Regular as a spring migrant since 1991 (ten or 11 records; only two previous spring records); the high seasonal total was four in 1992. A female at HCP 4-8 July 1995 was a very late spring migrant. One summer record of a singing second-year male at HCP 1 July-6 September 1995. Fall records average three or four per year. Nearly regular in winter, with a high seasonal total of four in 1984/85.

Prothonotary Warbler: Two spring records: ENC 17 May 1992 (female), and Laguna Beach 6 May 1993 (singing male). Five fall records: DBSP 8-11 October 1981; Westminster 27-29 September 1989; an early migrant in salt marsh habitat at BC 31 August 1991; Huntington Beach 16 September 1994; and HCP 17 September-6 October 1994.

Worm-eating Warbler: Two records of spring migrants: TRNC 11 May 1988, and HCP 7 May 1992. A fall migrant was in Westminster 1-6 November 1994 (*). One wintered at HCP 21 October 1987-3 February 1988.

Ovenbird: Six records of spring migrants: ENC 17-20 May 1984; Fullerton 2 June 1984 (struck window and recovered); SARM 9 May 1987; HCP 16 June 1988; Tustin 6 May 1991; and HCP 2 June 1991. Ten fall records, eight since 1981, with one early record: Huntington Beach 27-28 August 1994. One wintered at a private area in Costa Mesa 1-15 January 1994.

Northern Waterthrush: Seven records of apparent spring migrants, six since 1989. Records average three or four per fall, with a high seasonal total of eight to 12 in 1984. An early fall migrant was at HCP 15 August 1993; the latest apparent fall migrant was at DBSP 2 December 1989. Five winter records, two involving returning birds: DBSP 14 December 1980-17 January 1981; BR 31 December 1983-1 January 1984; SJM 30 December 1984 (DRW); BR 31 December 1989-1 January 1990, 8-26 April 1991, and 23 February 1992; and mouth of Bonita Creek 10 December 1992-7 March 1993, 1-28 January 1995, and 30 November 1995 +.

Louisiana Waterthrush: A singing male at HCP 3-6 May 1992 was the state's third record of a spring migrant.

Kentucky Warbler: Two records of wintering birds: a male in Corona del Mar 19 December 1983-6 March 1984, and an apparent immature male in South Laguna 17 December 1995-8 April 1996.

Mourning Warbler: One record of a fall migrant: HCP 5-20 September 1988 (immature). An adult male in Newport Beach 31 December 1994-25 February 1995 was California's second winter record.

MacGillivray's Warbler: This warbler is an uncommon spring and fall transient found primarily in brushy habitats of the coastal lowlands. Two records of presumed early spring migrants: Rose Canyon 26 March 1992, and HCP 27 March 1993. A late spring migrant was at OCNC 1 June 1989. Early fall migrants were at HCP 8 August 1992 and 13 August 1993. Four winter records: HCP 15 December 1980-11 January 1981; HCP 28 September 1985-22 March 1986, 9 October 1987-27 March 1988, and 24 October 1988-2 April 1989 (considered a single record); Newport Beach 6 February-1 April 1995; and CCSP 20 January 1996.

Common Yellowthroat: This warbler's status is more complex than its common year-round presence in the lowlands would suggest; for example, Unitt (1984) speculated that "possibly the wintering population [in San Diego County] is entirely different than the breeding population." In addition to the local breeder, *G.t. scirpicola*, LACM specimens exist for *G.t. occidentalis* (breeds in the Great Basin and Rocky Mountains) and *G.t. sinuosa* (breeds at San Francisco Bay; see van Rossem [1922]). Common Yellowthroats pass through high elevation riparian areas during spring and fall migrations, but the timing and magnitude of these movements are not well known.

Hooded Warbler: Twelve spring records, eight since 1989. Four fall records: UCI 23-30 October 1988; UCI 22 September 1990; Caspers Wilderness Park 3 November 1990; and a summering bird or very early migrant at HCP 13 August-13 September 1994. One in El Toro 15-16 December 1990 may have been a late fall migrant. One definite winter record of a male in Costa Mesa 31 December 1995-16 March 1996

Wilson's Warbler: This warbler is a common spring and fall transient and rare winter visitor. The earliest records of apparent spring migrants (or possibly lingering winter visitors) include UNB 5 March 1982; Santa Ana 10 March 1985; and OCNC 8 March 1990. A high count was 125 at HCP 13 May 1994 (LRH). One at OCNC 26 July 1979 was an early fall migrant. On average, three or four winter in the lowlands; the high seasonal total of eight has been recorded three times. Timing of departure for wintering birds is basically unknown.

Schneider (1900a) reported nesting at SARA, and it is likely that Wilson's Warbler nested in riparian woodlands county-wide during the early part of this century. Pequegnat (1951) termed it an "occasional summer resident in woodland vegetation around springs as high as 4500 feet." Extirpation of the local and regional breeding populations probably resulted from the inter-related phenomena of habitat destruction, habitat degradation and cowbird brood parasitism.

Canada Warbler: Eight fall records: Costa Mesa 24 September 1981; IRP 7 October 1984; HCP 13-15 September 1987; HCP 13-18 October 1988; SARM 18-19 October 1990; HCP 17-20 September 1993; Westminster 26-27 September 1993; and SJM 22-23 October 1994.

Painted Redstart: One record of a fall migrant: HCP 6 October 1989. Four winter records: Tustin Hills 17 December 1978 (inland CBC); San Clemente 25 November 1985-6 March 1986; a returning bird at Canyon Park, Costa Mesa, 5 December 1992-5 February 1993, 10 October 1993-13 March 1994, 25 September 1994-15 January 1995, and 5 October 1995-9 March 1996; and Huntington Beach 31 December 1995-17 March 1996.

Yellow-breasted Chat: This rare, localized summer resident breeds in dense willow-riparian habitat of the lowlands and foothills. Spring and fall migrants occur rarely in urban parks and similar settings. The earliest spring arrival was at BR 4 April 1991. Three records of late fall migrants: Santa Ana 16 October 1964, Costa Mesa 20 October 1990; and ENC 6-9 October 1995.

Hepatic Tanager: One spring record of a female at Santa Ana 28-31 May 1991. Two records of apparent fall migrants: SRAS 5-13 September 1973 (age/sex unknown), and DBSP 25 December 1982 (female or young male; BKS). Two winter records: a female at TRNC 1984/85 to 1987/88 (first observed 17 December 1984; the earliest arrival date was 22 October 1987 and the latest departure date was 13 April in both 1986 and 1987), and an immature male at UCI 21 November 1992-13 March 1993 that returned as an adult 14 November 1993-13 February 1994.

Summer Tanager: Thirteen spring records since 1983, the earliest at TRNC 6-9 May 1985. One summered at HCP in 1992. Records average approximately three per fall, and one to two per winter.

Scarlet Tanager: One spring record of an adult male at Capistrano Beach 5 June 1986. Six fall records: Dana Point 23 August 1964 (early; age/sex unknown); Tustin 15 November 1982 (age/sex unknown); immature male at HCP 25 November 1982; female at HCP 7-15 November 1987; female at HCP 10 November 1989; and immature male at Costa Mesa 12 November 1990.

Western Tanager: Field investigations in 1994 found Western Tanager to be a fairly common transient and rare, local summer resident in the major mountains canyons (e.g., UTC, upper Silverado Canyon), consistent with Pequegnat (1951) and G&D (1981). S&H (1979) erroneously called this migratory species a "fairly common, local resident" in the mountains.

Spring migrants are common from the coast to the foothills, arriving as early as 14 April (five males and a female at Trabuco Canyon in 1995). Fall migration is somewhat muted and primarily coastal, with two early records of fall migrants: TRNC 12 July 1984, and OCNC 4 July 1988. One at TRNC 23 June 1984 was unseasonal. Approximately five are found in an average winter, with a high total of 12 in 1989/90.

Rose-breasted Grosbeak: Eleven spring records, including five in 1992. Four summer/early fall records: San Juan Capistrano 25 July 1964; HCP 18 August-4 September 1986; HCP 29 July-4 August 1990; and HCP 4-8 July 1995. Fall records average about three per year. In addition to ten acceptable winter records, some older winter reports of Black-headed Grosbeak probably pertain to this species. An apparent Rose-breasted X Black-headed Grosbeak (adult male) was in Tustin 17-18 May 1983.

Black-headed Grosbeak: One at HCP 10 March 1984 was an exceptionally early spring migrant. Two acceptable winter records: Seal Beach 1 February 1987, and Huntington Beach 26 January 1995. Several poorly supported CBC records are not acceptable due to potential confusion with the similar Rose-breasted Grosbeak, which is more regular in southern California during winter.

Blue Grosbeak: Pequegnat (1951) considered this species "common along dry, Baccharis-dominated arroyos on the Pacific drainage below 1500 feet," giving an early arrival date of 2 April 1938 (location unspecified). S&H (1979) called it uncommon, with a "noticeable decline...from the species (sic) former abundance." Blue Grosbeaks remain uncommon overall, locally fairly common along well developed riparian corridors adjacent to extensive open areas (e.g., along portions of SDC and in the San Joaquin Hills). One at OCNC 3 December 1988 was apparently a late fall migrant. One definite winter record: IRP 29 February-9 March 1992.

Lazuli Bunting: Pequegnat (1951) considered this a "common summer visitant" to the mountains, noting birds "in Santiago Canyon as late as October 31" (record unacceptable, year not given). S&H (1979) characterized it as a fairly common breeder in the hills and mountains, and a fairly common migrant county-wide. This is still accurate, but it bears noting that Lazuli Buntings thrive in recently burned scrub and chaparral, and are characteristically among the most common nesting birds in such areas. Two records of early spring migrants: two at SJC 29 March 1986, and one at Rose Canyon 26 March 1992.

Indigo Bunting: Five records of spring migrants: near San Juan Capistrano 13 June 1965; HCP 4-6 May 1989; HCP 18 May 1989; HCP 5 May 1992; and HCP 25 May 1992. Since the first record of a fall migrant in 1981, this bunting has been recorded over twenty times in late summer/fall; a singing male at HCP 10-26 July 1995 was the earliest.

Painted Bunting: Three records of immature fall migrants: HCP 3 September 1993(*); HCP 17-18 September 1993 (*); and two at HCP 4 September to 24 October 1994 (*; the birds apparently arrived and departed together). The CBRC rejected a record of a male in alternate plumage at HCP 11-12 November 1988 due to questions of origin.

Dickcissel: Four records of fall migrants: DBSP 23 August 1981; TRNC 5 October 1983; Irvine 13 September 1993; and Irvine 21 September 1994.

Green-tailed Towhee: Twelve records of spring migrants since 1981, occurring 14 April to 14 May. Over 30 records of fall migrants since 1981, the vast majority in September; the earliest was at HCP 5-10 September 1988. Eleven records of wintering birds since 1979/80, the latest lingering at SBNWR until 1 April 1994.

Spotted Towhee: This colorful bird, formerly known as the Rufous-sided Towhee, is among the most abundant residents of chaparral, particularly in the Santa Ana Mountains. Migrants and post-breeding dispersants are occasionally found away from resident populations.

California Towhee: Common, widespread resident occupying a variety of natural and human-altered habitats county-wide.

Cassin's Sparrow: A singing, skylarking male was at BC 10-18 May 1986.

Rufous-crowned Sparrow: Fairly common resident, occurring primarily in broken sage scrub and scrub-grassland areas. Dispersing birds are occasionally noted away from resident populations (e.g., SARA 27 October 1984, San Clemente 28 August 1991).

American Tree Sparrow: One acceptable record of a wintering bird at Clark Regional Park 30 December 1989-28 January 1990.

Chipping Sparrow: This sparrow nests fairly commonly, but locally, around BJC. Migrants are uncommon in the lowlands and foothills, occurring primarily in April and September-October. One at HCP 20 May 1995 was a late spring migrant. In winter, Chipping Sparrow is locally common at IRP, generally uncommon elsewhere in the foothills, and rare in the lowlands. In recent years, flocks of ten or fewer have wintered at TRNC, Canyon Park in Costa Mesa, and Mile Square Park in Fountain Valley.

Clay-colored Sparrow: One at SJM 5 May 1991 was a spring migrant. Since 1987, records of fall migrants have averaged approximately three per year. Six acceptable winter records, four since 1989/90; the latest remained at OCNC until 12 April 1980.

Brewer's Sparrow: Eight records of spring migrants, seven since 1989 (the county's first was collected at Arch Beach 3 April 1888 #MVZ 76159). An average of one is seen each fall, with high seasonal totals of five in 1994 and four or five in 1995. Two records of early fall migrants: SJM 14 August 1993, and SARM 28 August 1993. Three acceptable winter records: YRP 15 January-3 March 1990; SARM 21 November 1993-22 January 1994; and MRP 15 December 1993.

Field Sparrow: Two records of wintering birds: IRP 25 November 1989-6 January 1990, and HCP 20 January-13 March 1994 (*).

Black-chinned Sparrow: This sparrow breeds fairly commonly in the mountains and foothills, uncommonly in the San Joaquin Hills; the earliest apparent arrival date is 7 March 1995 (one or two at WRP). Two records of spring migrants away from potential breeding habitat: SJM 12 April 1981, and Seal Beach 1 April 1986 (JSB). Four late fall/winter records: two in the vicinity of ONRP 28 December 1973 (inland CBC); one near Irvine Lake on the 1975, 1976 and 1978 inland CBCs (treated as one record); SORP 6 December 1983; and Signal Peak 13-14 November 1994.

Vesper Sparrow: Moderate numbers of this grassland sparrow wintered at PT before its development in the late 1980s; the high count was approximately 30 in 1981/82. Fewer than ten are now typically observed countywide during fall and winter, mostly in the San Joaquin Hills and interior foothills. The latest record is one at SRAS 15 April 1992.

Grinnell (1898) considered the larger, grayish "Western" (*P.g. confinis*) and smaller, brown/buffy "Oregon" (*P.g. affinis*) races to be common in the Los Angeles basin, with *confinis* occurring primarily in "stubble fields and washes, especially on the dry mesas," and *affinis* "possibly more numerous on the damper meadows of the lowlands." Unitt (1984) determined that "*confinis* is much more the frequent" in San Diego County, accounting for 15 of 17 local specimens at SDNHM. Although Orange County specimens are lacking, it is likely (and sight records suggest) that both races occur here regularly.

Lark Sparrow: This attractive sparrow is a fairly common resident in and around open coastal sage scrub, grasslands and rangelands. It is a rare, regular fall migrant to coastal areas unsuitable for breeding. Wintering birds are locally common at IRP and fairly common at other inland parks that include oaks and expanses of open turf.

Black-throated Sparrow: Five spring records: Huntington Beach "May 1974" (not graphed); Irvine 12 June 1979 (very late); CCSP 7 April 1987; Huntington Beach 23-25 April 1990; and Newport Beach 6 April 1992. One summer record of an exceptionally early dispersing juvenile at SARM 18 July 1992. Fourteen fall records, all since 1981 (15 August-19 September); six in 1993 was exceptional. Five acceptable late fall and winter records: ENC 18 March 1978; HCP 18 November 1981; OCNC 17 January 1986; SARA 21 January-11 February 1986; and VPB 3-11 December 1988. Details are lacking for one reported on the 1967 inland CBC.

Sage Sparrow: "Bell's" Sage Sparrow (*A.b. belli*) is an uncommon, local resident occurring primarily in chamisal chaparral of the Santa Ana Mountains. Although generally sedentary, localized fluctuations and population shifts seem to occur; successional (post-fire) habitats may be preferred. Sage Sparrows are rare in chaparral and coastal sage scrub of the interior foothills, and very rare in the San Joaquin Hills (e.g., Pelican Hill 5 July 1994). One was at SJM 28-30 October 1993 immediately following the Laguna Canyon Fire, which burned most of the San Joaquin Hills. An earlier out-of-range bird, an adult male apparently of the race *belli*, was collected at Seal Beach 5 July 1956 (#CSULB 1810).

Lark Bunting: One spring record: Stanton 10 April 1927 (Robertson 1927). Three fall records: Dana Point 1 September 1968; SJM 1-4 September 1987; and SARM 2 October 1993. One at CCSP 5 March 1988 probably wintered locally.

Savannah Sparrow: During fall and winter, migratory birds from a number of northern and interior subspecies (e.g., *P.s. nevadensis*) are common in a variety of grassland and marsh habitats throughout the lowlands.

The endangered "Belding's" race (*P.s. beldingi*) is a common resident of extensive pickleweed marshes along the coast.

The "Large-billed" race (*P.s. rostratus*), which breeds in the Colorado River delta, was once common in winter along beaches and coastal estuaries throughout the region (cf. G&M 1944). S&H (1979) stated that *rostratus* "winters commonly in Orange County," but this was apparently based on old data since G&D [1981] reported only one recent record from coastal southern California. In recent years, small numbers have been detected each year at SBNWR (high count of 11 on 4 November 1994), with a few records from BC and UNB. One at BC 14 June 1992 (RAE) was unseasonal, and one at SJM 28 August 1994 was away from typical coastal strand habitat.

Grasshopper Sparrow: This grassland specialist nests fairly commonly but locally in the county's remaining extensive grasslands, including portions of the San Joaquin Hills and southern foothills. Two singing in the San Joaquin Hills 26 February 1995 were the earliest apparent arrivals. Four records of fall migrants away from open grassland habitat: MRP 1 November 1987; UNB 25 November 1989; HCP 31 October 1992; and HCP 2 September 1994. Small numbers are found in grasslands most winters, but the status remains somewhat uncertain due to detection difficulties.

Le Conte's Sparrow: One winter record: UNB 14 December 1993-11 January 1994 (*).

Nelson's Sharp-tailed Sparrow: Eleven records from UNB since the first record on 17 October 1970, with a high count of up to four or five in 1993/94. Birds typically depart by late January, but have been recorded as late as 14 March 1977. Nelson's and Saltmarsh sharp-tailed sparrows were formerly considered conspecific. It is likely, and sight records suggest, that our wintering birds belong to the brightly colored "Interior" group, consisting of the races *A.n. nelsoni* and *A.n. alterus* (cf. Sibley 1996).

Fox Sparrow: Refining taxonomic concepts set forth by Swarth (1920) and Linsdale (1928), Zink (1994) analyzed 16 subspecies within four field-identifiable groups that he considers species; Rising (1996) covers identification of these groups. Sight records exist for one or more subspecies within each group, but relatively little effort has been made to determine their local distribution or relative abundance. The graphs and following remarks provide our best estimations of each group's overall status.

Within the rusty, streak-backed "Red" group, *P.i. zaboria* has been recorded twice in fall: TRNC 3-4 November 1982, and IRP 14 November 1992 (BED).

Within the warm brown, plain-backed "Sooty" group, *P.i. unalaschcensis* winters uncommonly to fairly commonly in the mountains, and uncommonly in the foothills and lowlands; numbers vary substantially from year to year, at least in the lowlands. Also within this group, several particularly dark birds possibly belonging to *P.i. fuliginosa* have been observed at HCP in October/November (BED).

Within the small-billed, grayish-backed "Slate-colored" group, the brown-and-gray *P.i. schistacea* is fairly common to common in higher elevation chaparral, uncommon in the interior foothills, and rare elsewhere; an early fall migrant was at HCP 11 September 1994. Also within this group, the rufescent, indistinctly streak-backed *P.i. altivagans* appears to be uncommon in the lowlands and fairly common to common in the foothills and mountains.

Large-billed, gray-backed birds belonging to the "Thick-billed" group, including *P.i. megarhynchus* and *P.i. stephensi*, appear to be fairly common to common in the Santa Ana Mountains and uncommon in the foothills. Two lowland records: HCP 23 October 1991 (BED), and coastal bluff scrub near SARM 29 March 1994 (RAH).

Pequegnat (1951) reported two Fox Sparrows of unspecified race at Modjeska Springs "as late as 24 May 1940" (not graphed).

Song Sparrow: The "San Diego" Song Sparrow (*M.m. cooperi*) is a common permanent resident of marshes, riparian scrub, mesic chaparral and densely landscaped areas from the coast to the foothills, always near water. In riparian thickets of the mountains, Song Sparrow is a locally fairly common breeder, rare in winter, found as high as 3000 feet. Several additional subspecies potentially occur during migration and winter, but no research has been conducted to determine this.

Lincoln's Sparrow: This sparrow is a fairly common to common migrant and winter resident found primarily in moist, often weedy areas. In March and April transients are found in a wider diversity of habitats than is typical for fall and winter. Three records of early fall migrants: DBSP 23 August 1981; HCP 5 September 1988; and HCP 29 August 1994. Pequegnat (1951) reported catching one in a rodent trap on Santiago Peak 11 January 1941.

Swamp Sparrow: On average, approximately four are seen each fall/winter; ten during winter 1993/94 was a high seasonal total. Two early fall records on successive days: IRP 6 October 1990, and UCI 7 October 1990.

White-throated Sparrow: Fall/winter records average approximately three per year, the birds generally associating with White-crowned Sparrows. Seven or eight during winter 1990/91 was a high seasonal total.

Golden-crowned Sparrow: This sparrow is common only in woodlands and moist chaparral of foothill and mountain canyons; it is generally uncommon in the coastal lowlands, although moderate flocks may be found along creeks and in other particularly moist, densely vegetated habitat areas.

White-crowned Sparrow: The rufous-and-gray-backed, orange-billed *Z.l. gambelii* is abundant in the lowlands and common in the foothills and mountains. Two records of late spring migrants: two at SJM 13 May 1995, and one at HCP 20 May 1995. One at HCP 4 September 1988 was presumably an early fall migrant, while one at HCP 13-29 August 1993 possibly summered locally.

The brown-and-black-backed, yellowish-billed *Z.l. pugetensis* is a rare, regular winter visitor in the lowlands within a few miles of the coast; it is reported less regularly inland to the foothills of the Santa Ana Mountains.

Three spring records of dark-lored birds presumably belonging to *Z.l. oriantha*: Buena Park 1 May 1929; Huntington Beach 15 May 1990; and Seal Beach 26 May 1994. One fall record: MRP 29 October 1995. An apparent hybrid, with one dark lore and one light lore, was observed at IRP 3 December 1994 (MTH pers. comm.). Robertson (1933) reported the 1929 Buena Park record as *leucophrys* before *oriantha* had been described, apparently giving rise to the claim in S&H (1979) that *leucophrys* occurs in Orange County.

A late White-crowned Sparrow in Costa Mesa 22 May 1964 was not identified to race (not graphed).

Harris' Sparrow: Four records of possible spring migrants: Buena Park 23-27 April 1938; San Clemente 4 May 1969; Garden Grove 27 March-2 April 1981; and Huntington Beach 23-30 April 1983. Nine winter records, seven since 1981.

Dark-eyed Junco: "Oregon Juncos" (*J.h. oreganus* group) breed fairly commonly in the higher mountains and rarely in oak woodlands of the foothills (e.g., SRAS); in the lowlands, a pair nested at HCP in 1992 and 1993. Wintering flocks are scattered liberally around the county, but are most common in the mountains and in oak woodlands throughout. These flocks often include one or more "Slate-colored Juncos" (*J.h. hyemalis* group), although this race may be hard to find during certain years.

Records of "Gray-headed Junco" (*J.h. caniceps* group) average one or two per fall/winter in the lowlands and foothills; it is to be looked for in the mountains.

Wintering "Pink-sided Juncos" (*J.h. mearnsi*) have been recorded twice: IRP 16 December 1989-16 February 1990, and Craig Regional Park 23-29 January 1994.

McCown's Longspur: Five late fall/winter records: one at PT 28 November 1986-11 January 1987; one at UCI 19 October-3 November 1990, with a second bird present 26-29 October; two at PT 16 December 1990; and one in Irvine 29 October 1991.

Lapland Longspur: Since 1988, individuals and flocks of up to four birds have been recorded annually during fall and/or winter; most records are from November and early December. The earliest fall migrant was at PT 8 October 1989. This longspur has been detected four times after mid-December, and has lingered as late as 28 February 1992 (one or two at PT).

Chestnut-collared Longspur: PT supported impressive mixed flocks of Horned Larks and longspurs before its development in the early 1990s; the high count of Chestnut-collareds was 75 on 26 December 1976 (the county's first record). Individuals and flocks typically containing fewer than ten birds now occur at scattered locations. Three records of birds remaining into March: approximately ten at PT 15 March 1987; approximately 25 at PT 1 March 1990; and one in Los Alamitos 14 March 1995.

Bobolink: Three records of spring migrants: a singing male was briefly encountered in salt marsh habitat at SBNWR during "early May" in the mid-1970s (CTC, BWM pers. comms.; not graphed); a male was at SJM 30 May 1984; and a singing male was at SJM 25 May 1991. Fall records average greater than one per year, although it is missed some years; at least 12 during fall 1994 was a high seasonal total. One at SJM 27 October 1985 was late.

Red-winged Blackbird: Common permanent resident, nesting primarily in emergent vegetation at freshwater marshes, ponds and reservoirs. There is a significant post-breeding influx from outside the county, and immense fall and winter foraging flocks of Red-winged Blackbirds, often together with other icterids, may be found in agricultural fields, rangelands and other expansive open spaces.

Tricolored Blackbird: Nesting and wintering numbers of this nomadic blackbird fluctuate widely from year to year, although its flocking habits and localized occurrence preclude characterizing the county-wide status as "rare" or "common" in any given year. Gallagher (1993) reported several dense, localized nesting colonies scattered throughout the county, including many in city parks (e.g., Carr Park in Huntington Beach and Tewinkle Park in Costa Mesa). The larger colonies (e.g., Cañada Chiquita, SDC, PCRP) are typically located near expansive grasslands or agricultural fields, and may contain as many as 750 pairs each. Feeding flocks of 1000 or more birds are occasionally encountered in fall and winter.

Western Meadowlark: Locally common breeder in rangelands and open fields. Meadowlarks become more common and widespread in the winter months, but the timing of this influx is poorly known. Pequegnat (1951) termed this a "common resident in grassland and sagebrush belts and in openings in chaparral as high as 3000 feet," but recent observers have not found meadowlarks in such areas.

Yellow-headed Blackbird: Small nesting colonies are periodically found in marshy areas (e.g., "several pairs" at Los Alamitos Golf Course 16 June 1989). Approximately 100 near Irvine 30 January 1987 was a high count. Spring migrants often occur in April and early May, fall migrants in September.

Rusty Blackbird: Three acceptable late fall/winter records: near Santa Ana 31 December 1962-26 January 1963; Seal Beach 8-9 December 1991; and Irvine 6 February-12 March 1994 (see Hamilton 1995). McCaskie (1971) and S&H (1979) published one from DBSP 2 October 1963, but this record is considered unacceptable since supporting details are lacking (GM and EAP pers. comms.) and the date is very early for the region.

Brewer's Blackbird: Common permanent resident, occupying more or less open, natural and human-altered habitats throughout the lowlands and foothills. The species becomes more abundant in fall and winter, when migrants and winter visitors from outside the county form large feeding flocks in agricultural fields, rangelands, and developed areas.

Great-tailed Grackle: First recorded in 1981, numbers are steadily increasing as part of a region-wide incursion. A pair nested at SARA in 1982, followed by a group of eight females and three males three miles upriver from the initial nesting site in 1984. More recently, grackles have nested at HCP (two pairs in 1994) and along Peters Canyon Channel in Irvine (pair with three begging young 21 August 1994). The high count is 26 at HCP during fall 1995.

Brown-headed Cowbird: This brood-parasite winters in and around urban and suburban neighborhoods, golf courses, agricultural areas and stables, then moves into native plant communities during the nesting season to lay their eggs in the nests of songbirds. The greatest numbers seem to be found in expansive, somewhat disturbed lowland and foothill riparian woodlands. Many of the cowbirds that breed in Orange County probably winter elsewhere. This bird's human-assisted expansion in the West, first noted in the early 1900s, has contributed to major declines in numerous bird populations associated with riparian habitats statewide (Laymon 1987, Rothstein 1994).

Orchard Oriole: One record of a definite spring migrant: HCP 27-30 May 1989 (female). Records average approximately one per year in late fall/winter, the vast majority wintering locally. Two early records: adult male at Dana Point 12 August to "late October" 1964, observed there again 11-22 April 1965 (taken to be the same bird wintering); and ENC 14 September 1991.

Hooded Oriole: As a breeder, this oriole is found fairly commonly in suburban and rural areas, often in palms; it is generally uncommon in lowland riparian areas during summer. Pequegnat (1951) termed it a "common summer visitant to canyons below 3000 feet," but Hooded Oriole is not presently known to breed in District 3. Winter records average approximately one per year, although it is occasionally missed.

Baltimore Oriole: Rare late fall migrant and winter visitor, averaging about one record per year. One at HCP 19 September 1986 was an early fall migrant. Individuals at UCI 9 April 1989 and ENC 10-16 April 1989 were either wintering birds or spring migrants. Three records of apparent spring migrants: two at Laguna Beach 1 June 1969; one at Newport Beach 11 May 1992; and one at HCP 11 May 1993. Baltimore and Bullock's orioles were formerly classified together as the Northern Oriole.

Bullock's Oriole: This oriole nests commonly in well developed riparian woodlands; it particularly favors tall California Sycamores (*Platanus racemosa*). Winter records average approximately eight per year, usually in and around blooming eucalyptus. Bullock's and Baltimore orioles were formerly classified together as the Northern Oriole.

Scott's Oriole: Winter records average approximately two per year in the interior foothills, many of these at Ramakrishna Monastery in Live Oak Canyon (visiting hours 9-11 a.m. & 3-5 p.m.). The earliest arrival was one at SORP 21 October 1982; up to four wintering birds remained at Ramakrishna Monastery until 23 May 1981. Three records of lingering birds or spring migrants: Santa Ana 10 April 1948; one to two at OCNC 27 April-5 May 1984; and one in Laguna Canyon 5 May. Scott's Oriole is unrecorded on the coastal CBC.

Purple Finch: This finch is a fairly common, somewhat localized, resident of oak and coniferous woodlands of the mountains. Small numbers have been found in oaks and pines of the foothills (Trabuco Canyon, SRAS, SJC) during spring and summer, but the breeding status is unknown. In winter, Purple Finch is rare to fairly common in the foothills, absent to uncommon in the lowlands.

House Finch: This finch is a ubiquitous resident of natural and developed areas from the coast to the lower mountain canyons. Numbers are greatly reduced in areas of expansive chaparral and in the higher mountains.

Red Crossbill: Small numbers are typically detected only during rare "irruption" years. Swarth (1908) "distinctly heard" one at UTC 18 September 1908 (early). A high daily count was 23 at ONRP 22 November 1987.

Pine Siskin: Siskins often travel in mixed flocks with goldfinches. They are rare to absent some years, but are fairly common and widespread during occasional regional "irruption" years. One at UTC 13 September 1995 was very early. Recent CBC totals are representative of this species' irregular winter status: in 1990 and 1991 it went unrecorded on the coastal and inland CBCs, while the 1992 and 1994 inland CBCs tallied 141 and 184 respectively.

Lesser Goldfinch: This goldfinch is a common permanent resident from the coast to the mountains, occupying all but the most thoroughly urbanized areas.

Lawrence's Goldfinch: This often elusive goldfinch is most common and widespread in March and April. High counts include 150-200 at TRNC 23 February 1982 and 75 in the Santa Ana Mountains 21 November 1993. In recent years, small numbers have nested regularly at TRNC and irregularly elsewhere.

American Goldfinch: Pequegnat (1951) reported that this goldfinch "apparently breeds occasionally in sycamores in canyons [of the Santa Ana Mountains, but is] much more common during winter months." Gallagher (1993) reported nesting only in willow dominated riparian areas below 800 feet. American Goldfinches are somewhat more widespread in winter, but still occur primarily in the lowlands and foothills.

Supplemental List

The following reports of native species lack documentation that we consider adequate, or pertain to birds at locations where the potential for human release is relatively high. Each warrants mention nonetheless, as one or more record may prove to be acceptable later (e.g., depending on votes of the CBRC). The "hypothetical species" list in S&H (1979) contains several unsubstantiated reports that we have not repeated here.

Leach's Storm-Petrel (*Oceanodroma leucorhoa*): A total of ten were reported "in the San Pedro Channel" 3 May 1964; if identified correctly, these birds were probably not in county waters as defined in this book. Four storm-petrels off NP 19 September 1993 under calm wind conditions exhibited flight behaviors that two experienced observers considered characteristic of Leach's Storm-Petrel. This record is considered hypothetical based on 1) the species' general fidelity to the far offshore waters (e.g., G&D 1981 stated that "storm-petrels inside the islands and in inshore waters are virtually never of this species"), and 2) identification based on flight characteristics alone.

American Anhinga (*Anhinga anhinga*): Johnson (1990) reported one at UNB "one winter" during the period 1940-1955 (ø) but did not provide substantiating details. Two female/immature-types were reported circling over Westminster 2 November 1994 (*), and a female was reported flying over SJM 30 July 1995 (*). Written descriptions for the 1994 and 1995 records are convincing, but this species' natural occurrence in coastal southern California is questionable; we defer judgment of these records to the CBRC.

White Ibis (*Eudocimus albus*): A probable escapee was at SJM 29 July-26 August 1979.

Black-bellied Whistling-Duck (*Dendrocygna autumnalis*): The CBRC unanimously rejected one of unspecified age at SJM 18-28 July 1970 on the basis of questionable origin. Apparently referring to the same bird, Audubon Field Notes (24:716) reported that an adult was at SJM 28 July-1 August 1970. Citing this reference, S&H (1979 p. 71) erroneously reported "birds at SJM in August, 1969." Todd (1979) reported this species to be commonly kept in captivity, and S&H (1979) mentioned the existence of pinioned Black-bellied Whistling-Ducks at Lion Country Safari.

Falcated Teal (*Anas falcata*): A record of a likely escapee at UNB 2 January-21 February 1969 is on the CBRC's "Supplemental List."

Harris' Hawk (*Parabuteo unicinctus*): A very tame bird was at UCI 10-12 December 1994, and PHB (pers. comm.) reports periodic occurrences, all of which he considers likely released/escaped birds (i.e., they do not appear to be part of the recent, apparently natural incursion of Harris' Hawks into the interior of southern California). Still, there is a chance that this hawk has reached Orange County without human assistance.

Red-legged Kittiwake (*Rissa brevirostris*): An adult male found sick in an Anaheim apartment complex 28 February 1996 subsequently died in captivity (#LACM 109199). If accepted by the CBRC, this would represent a first state record. This bird's occurrence outside of reasonably suitable habitat, however, raises questions regarding the potential for it to have arrived unassisted. In the hierarchy of improbable vagrants found in Orange County, an acceptable record of Red-legged Kittiwake, particularly one from Anaheim, would have to share top billing with records of White-tailed Tropicbird and Ivory Gull discussed in the main body of this book.

Tufted Puffin (*Fratercula cirrhata*): A sick bird reported as a first-year Tufted Puffin was observed approximately five miles southwest of Newport Harbor on 15 March 1993. Although it was felt that the bird was probably identified correctly, the date is over a month earlier than most spring records south of Monterey County (G&D 1981) and the supporting details were judged inadequate to document this as the first county record.

Northern Pygmy-Owl (*Glaucidium gnoma*): S&H (1979) reported this pygmy-owl to be "rare in the live oaks or sycamores in canyons...possibly resident...although mostly noted December-February." The species is occasionally reported from potentially suitable habitat in the mountains, but details have been inadequate to confirm identification. Since Orange County is outside of the known range of Northern Pygmy-Owl, and its calls may be confused with the Northern Saw-whet Owl (a rare resident), its occurrence is considered unconfirmed.

Pinyon Jay (*Gymnorhinus cyanocephalus*): One was probably heard over Hicks Canyon 29 September 1995, but the bird was not seen and those involved considered the encounter inconclusive.

Cassin's Finch (*Carpodacus cassinii*): S&H (1979) called this montane finch a "rare, irregular winter visitor, mainly in canyons with Purple and House finches; seldom seen in the coastal lowlands." While Cassin's Finches almost certainly reach the Santa Ana Mountains very rarely, definite records are lacking. Museum records at CSULB indicate that several putative Cassin's Finches were collected from the Santa Ana Mountains, but the only extant specimen was found to be a Purple Finch. We are unwilling to publish this species' occurrence in the county without substantiating details.

Introduced and Exotic Species

As Orange County's natural landscape began its transformation first to agricultural fields and then sprawling urban "forests" and "savannahs" of exotic trees and shrubs, a variety of non-native avian species found the new habitats to their liking. Many species were locally introduced, either intentionally or unintentionally (e.g., several parrot species), while others likely spread into the area from introductions much further afield (e.g., European Starling). Four species, Rock Dove, Spotted Dove, European Starling and House Sparrow, are widespread, occupying major portions of the county altered by human activities. To varying degrees, these species also occur in surrounding natural areas where they 1) compete with native species for necessities like food, cover and nesting space, and 2) potentially expand the prey base available to raptors and other predators. As such, these alien species may play important ecological roles in the areas they inhabit.

The list of exotic birds that have been observed free-flying in the county would undoubtedly be quite extensive. While some of these species are known to nest occasionally, most fail to establish stable populations. The following species accounts discuss non-native species known to be, or suspected of being, reasonably established in the county (i.e., species with self-sustaining populations and only minor recruitment of released or escaped individuals). As local birders are only beginning to study exotic birds with any sense of purpose, the following discussions undoubtedly cover only a fraction of the "reasonably established" populations.

Readers are encouraged to help fill the holes in our collective understanding of these species by taking careful notes on exotic species, particularly those that appear to be establishing local populations. Written accounts, including as much detail as possible and return address/phone number, should be mailed to Audubon House (P.O. Box 5447, Irvine, CA 92616-5447). These accounts will be kept on file for researchers. Information on kinds and numbers of birds kept in captivity (locally or elsewhere) is also very useful in judging the validity of unusual records that potentially pertain to naturally occurring vagrants. This information should also be sent to Audubon House.

Species Accounts

Canada Goose (*Branta canadensis*): As noted in the primary species account in the main body of this book, releases of Canada Geese statewide bring an element of uncertainty to determining their status (PFS pers. comm.); for example, a pair of *moffitti* with three young on SDC 2 June 1989 (RAH) almost certainly originated from captive stock.

Egyptian Goose (*Alopochen aegyptiacus*): During the last decade, this goose seems to have become firmly established at many neighborhood parks and golf courses throughout the county, especially where open water is available. Occupied sites include Mile Square Regional Park, YRP, HCP, MRP/Rancho San Joaquin Golf Course, Santa Ana River Lakes, Anaheim Lake, Los Alisos Water Treatment Plant in Lake Forest and Marbella Golf Course in San Juan Capistrano.

Wood Duck (*Aix sponsa*): Introductions and/or dispersants from artificially established resident populations are increasingly common in the lowlands and foothills (see the species account in the main body of this book).

Mandarin Duck (*Aix galericulata*): A small colony containing perhaps a dozen birds is resident along lower SDC adjacent to and below SJM. S&H (1979) reported that a male was shot "near SJM" in 1973, suggesting that this population has been established for over two decades. These birds have given rise to some reports of the similar Wood Duck from this area (although note that Wood Ducks were recently released at SJM).

Mallard (*Anas platyrhynchos*): As mentioned in the earlier species account, crosses with ducks and geese are common in parks and some natural areas (e.g., UNB, SARA) county-wide.

Ring-necked Pheasant (*Phasianus colchicus*): S&H (1979) considered this pheasant to be "established fairly commonly, locally around county." A juvenal female was taken at Buena Park 22 May 1954 (#CSULB 1081) and adult male was taken at Seal Beach 26 April 1956 (#CSULB 1707). Local populations appear to have been eliminated by development of the county's once extensive agricultural lands. Escapees or intentionally released birds are still occasionally encountered.

Common Peafowl (*Pavo cristatus*): A population introduced at IRP in the 1920s presently includes approximately 75 birds. Smaller populations exist elsewhere in the county's interior (e.g., Trabuco Canyon, Lemon Heights, and the vicinity of SORP).

Rock Dove (*Columba livia*): Common to abundant resident found in the vicinity of human habitation and agricultural areas. In Orange County, as elsewhere, this adaptable dove nests on a variety of human structures and on sea cliffs (Gallagher 1993).

Spotted Dove (*Streptopelia chinensis*): This Asian dove is a fairly common resident of suburban neighborhoods throughout much of the county, with greatest numbers occurring in northern and western areas.

Red-crowned Parrot (*Amazona viridigenalis*): The status of this parrot is somewhat unclear due to confusion with the similar Lilac-crowned Parrot.

Red-crowneds appear to be well established in the north-central portion of the County, including Anaheim, Orange, Tustin, Santa Ana and Garden Grove. Flocks of up to several dozen individuals (which may also include Lilac-crowned Parrots) are frequently encountered in Santa Ana and Orange, with occasional concentrations numbering well over 100 birds. As with other species of parrot and parakeet, Red-crowned Parrots primarily frequent neighborhoods with an abundance of fruit or nut bearing trees.

Lilac-crowned Parrot (*Amazona finschi*): The status is uncertain due to this parrot's similarity to Red-crowned Parrot, with which it may associate. Lilac-crowned Parrot is apparently established in north-central Orange County. A small flock of Amazona parrots, containing Lilac-crowned and/or Red-crowned parrots, has recently been observed at IRP.

Yellow-headed Parrot (*Amazona oratrix*): Small numbers may be established in Santa Ana, and recent reports have come from Huntington Beach and the Newport Beach/Costa Mesa area. This species has declined significantly in the Los Angeles Basin since the 1960s and 1970s (KLG pers. comm.). Formerly reported in Anaheim.

Monk Parakeet (*Myiopsitta monachus*): A presumed roost nest with at least five birds present was discovered in Anaheim in October 1973, with a few potential subsequent sightings in Santa Ana and Orange (S&H 1979). RAE observed up to four in San Clemente from April through August 1991. This parakeet is not presently known to be established in Orange County, but colonies of this very adaptable species would not be unexpected.

Black-hooded Parakeet (*Nandayus nenday*): Small populations are known from Huntington Beach and Garden Grove.

Mitred Parakeet (*Aratinga mitrata*): This parakeet has been recently observed in San Clemente, Garden Grove, Orange, Santa Ana and Corona del Mar, but it is not known if populations are well established. A population is currently established in Long Beach, Los Angeles County (KLG pers. comm.).

European Starling (*Sturnus vulgaris*): First recorded locally in the early 1950s, this species rapidly spread throughout the county. An early specimen was collected one mile north of Dana Point 6 February 1954 (#CSULB 577), and a juvenal female was taken at Laguna Beach 2 June 1955 (#CSULB 1632). Ten birds were recorded on local CBCs in 1959, a total that jumped to 1142 by 1964. The species is now abundant from the coast to the foothills, with small numbers extending locally into the mountains. In winter, the resident population is augmented by significant numbers of migrants from outside the county. By far, the largest numbers occur in the vicinity of human habitation and in agricultural areas.

Aggressive and highly adaptable by nature, European Starlings have displaced many native cavity nesting birds in the lowlands and foothills. In Orange County, Western Bluebirds may have experienced the most significant starling-related decline.

House Sparrow (*Passer domesticus*): First recorded in the county at Buena Park 15 April, 1912 (Robertson 1924). House Sparrows are now ubiquitous throughout urban and suburban Orange County, sometimes foraging in adjacent natural areas. They may also be found in rural settings that include human structures (e.g., barns, houses, bridges) for nesting. For additional information see Robbins 1973.

Northern Red Bishop (*Euplectes franciscanus*): A pair with young was observed at SARM in spring 1994 (RAH) and summer 1995 (JEP), and up to two males were observed in Irvine agricultural fields in fall 1994. Individuals are occasionally encountered elsewhere.

Nutmeg Mannikin (*Lonchura punctulata*): Small numbers have present at HCP since around 1990, with ten to 15 pairs nesting successfully there in 1994 and 1995.

Additional Species

Among the wide variety of exotic birds observed individually or in groups (including many species of waterfowl, parrot, parakeet, estrellid finch and other small songbird groups that may, in fact, be locally established), the following species warrant mention due to a relatively high frequency of reports: Mute Swan (*Cygnus olor*), Budgerigar (*Melopsittacus undulatus*), Chestnut Mannikin (*Lonchura malacca*) and European Goldfinch (*Carduelis carduelis*). Two records of Greater Flamingo (*Phoenicopterus ruber*) almost certainly pertain to escapees: BC "late July through August" 1958 (after one escaped from Marineland on the Palos Verdes Peninsula in late July 1958), and UNB 25 September 1960.

Literature Cited and Selected References

The following list includes literature cited herein plus a number of additional references relevant to bird life in Orange County. Many of the following citations were culled from the extensive reference lists in Sexton and Hunt (1979) and Gallagher (1993), local works that are recommended to readers seeking additional information on the local avifauna. Jehl and Johnson (1994) is a collection of recent scientific papers describing avian population trends in the West. Thelander and Crabtree (1994) provides a useful overview of conservation threats to California wildlife species and their habitats. Readers interested in expanding their literary horizons beyond the "Orange Curtain" are directed to Webster (1993).

Ainley, D.G., W.J. Sydeman, S.A. Hatch, and U.W. Wilson. 1994. Seabird population trends along the west coast of North America: causes and the extent of regional concordance. Pp. 119-133 *in* J.R. Jehl, Jr., and N.K. Johnson (eds.), A century of avifaunal change in western North America. Studies in Avian Biology No. 15.

Allen, R.A. 1984. Natural vegetation of Orange County. Memoirs of the Natural History Foundation of Orange County 1:1-11.

American Ornithologists' Union. 1957. Check-list of North American Birds, fifth ed. American Ornithologists' Union, Baltimore.

----- 1983. Check-list of North American Birds, sixth ed. American Ornithologists' Union. Washington, DC.

----- 1985. Thirty-fifth supplement to the A.O.U. Check-list of North American Birds. Auk 102:680-686.

----- 1987. Thirty-sixth supplement to the A.O.U. Check-list of North American Birds. Auk 104:591-596.

----- 1989. Thirty-seventh supplement to the A.O.U. Check-list of North American Birds. Auk 106:532-538.

----- 1991. Thirty-eighth supplement to the A.O.U. Check-list of North American Birds. Auk 108:680-686.

----- 1993. Thirty-ninth supplement to the A.O.U. Check-list of North American Birds. Auk 110:675-682.

----- 1996. Fortieth supplement to the A.O.U. Check-list of North American Birds. Auk 112:819-830.

Atwood, J.L. 1980. The United States distribution of the California Black-tailed Gnatcatcher. Western Birds 11:65-78.

----- 1988. Speciation and Geographic Variation in Black-tailed Gnatcatchers (*Polioptila californica*). Ornithological Monograph No. 42.

----- 1990. Status review of the California Gnatcatcher (*Polioptila californica*). Manomet Bird Observatory, P.O. Box 1770, Manomet, Mass. 02345.

----- 1992. A maximum estimate of the California Gnatcatcher's population size in the United States. Western Birds 23:1-9.

----- 1994. Rare, local, little-known, and declining North American breeders, a closer look: California Gnatcatcher. Birding 24:229-234.

Austin, G.T. 1971. On the occurrence of eastern wood warblers in western North America. Condor 73:455-462.

Bailey, F.M. 1907. White-throated Swifts at Capistrano. Condor 9:169-172.

Bangs, O. 1899. A new rail from southern California. New England Zoological Club, Proceedings 1:45-46.

Beezley, J.A., and J.P. Rieger. 1987. Least Bell's Vireo management by cowbird trapping. Western Birds 18:55-61.

Behle, W.H. 1950. Clines in the yellow-throats of western North America. Condor 52:193-219.

Belding, L. 1890. Land birds of the Pacific district. California Academy of Sciences Occasional Paper No. 2.

Binford, L.C., and D.B. Johnson. 1995. Range expansion of the Glaucous-winged Gull into interior United States and Canada. Western Birds 26(4): 169-188.

Bloom, P.H. 1994. The biology and current status of the Long-eared Owl in coastal southern California. Bulletin of the Southern California Academy of Sciences 93:1-12.

Bock, C.E., and L.W. Lepthien. 1974. Winter patterns of bird species diversity and abundance in the U.S. and Canada. American Birds 28:556-562.

Bontrager, D.R. 1974. Breeding bird census: Sycamore-Coast Live Oak riparian woodland. American Birds 28:1035-1036.

----- 1991 (unpublished report). Habitat requirements, home range, and breeding biology of the California Gnatcatcher (*Polioptila californica*) in south Orange County. Copy in Van Tyne Library, Univ. of Michigan, Ann Arbor 48109.

Bontrager, D.R., R.A. Erickson, and R.A. Hamilton. 1995. Impacts of the October 1993 Laguna Canyon Fire on California Gnatcatchers and Cactus Wrens. *in* J.E. Keeley and T.A. Scott (eds.), Brushfires in California: Ecology and Resource Management. International Association of Wildland Fire, Fairfield, Washington.

Briggs, K.T., W.B. Tyler, D.B. Lewis, and D.R. Carlson. 1987. Bird communities at sea off California: 1975 to 1983. Studies in Avian Biology No. 11.

Burnham, H., W.M. Pierce, and H. White. 1917. Preliminary list of birds from the Claremont-Laguna region. Journal of Entomology & Zoology (Pomona College) 9:45-65.

Butler, R. 1990. The status of wintering Canada Geese at Quail Hill. Memoirs of the Natural History Foundation of Orange County 3:56-62.

Calder, J.A. 1926. Say Phoebe banded at night. Condor 28:50.

California Burrowing Owl Consortium. 1993. Burrowing Owl survey protocol and mitigation guidelines. Copy on file at Sea & Sage Audubon House, Irvine.

Carter, H.R., G.J. McChesney, D.L. Jaques, C.S. Strong, M.W. Parker, J.E. Takekawa, D.L. Jory, and D.L. Whitworth. 1992. Breeding populations of seabirds in California, 1989-1991. Unpublished draft report, U.S. Fish and Wildlife Service, Dixon, Calif.

Cheltan, D.B., P.A. Bernal, and J.A. McGowan. 1982. Large-scale interannual physical and biological interaction in the California current. Journal of Marine Research 40(4):1095-1125.

Collins, C.T., W.A. Schew, and E. Burkett. 1991. Elegant Terns breeding in Orange County, California. American Birds 45:393-395.

Collins, C.T. 1996 (in prep.). Hybridization of a Sandwich Tern and Elegant Tern in California. Submittal to Western Birds expected.

Collins, C.T., and and K.L. Garrett. 1996. The Black Skimmer in California: an overview. Western Birds 27(3):127-135.

Cooper, J.G. 1870. Geological survey of California. Ornithology. S.F. Baird, ed. University Press, Cambridge, Mass.

Daggett, F.S. 1901. Stragglers in southern California. Condor 3:15.

Daugherty, C.H. 1941a. The Season. Southern California Region. Audubon May-June, Sect. II:318.

----- 1941b. The Season. Southern California Region. Audubon July-August, Sect. II:398.

Davis, E. 1897. Nesting of the Bald Eagle in Orange County, California. Nidologist 4(7):78-79. Copy on file at Sea & Sage Audubon House, Irvine.

Dawson, W.L. 1923. The Birds of California. Vols. 1-4. South Moulton Company, San Diego.

DeRuff, R. 1990. The plants of Upper Newport Bay, 1982-1989. Memoirs of the Natural History Foundation of Orange County 3:10-19.

DeSante, D., and P. Pyle. 1986. Distributional Checklist of North American Birds. Artemisia Press, Lee Vining, Calif.

DeSante, D.F. 1983. Annual variability in the abundance of migrant landbirds on Southeast Farallon Island, California. Auk 100:826-852.

Devillers, P., R.G. McCaskie, and J.R. Jehl, Jr. 1971. The distribution of certain large gulls (*Larus*) in southern California and Baja California. California Birds 2(1):11-26.

Dittman, D., and G. Lasley. 1992. How to document rare birds. Birding 24:145-159.

Dixon, J. 1906. Land birds of San Onofre, California. Condor 8:91-98.

Dunn, H.H. 1897. Notes on a few southern California birds. Oologist 14:67-68.

----- 1899. The kingbirds of southern California. The Museum 5:154-155.

----- 1901. The Spotted Owl (*Syrinium occidentale*). Oologist 18:165-167.

Dunn, J.L., K.L. Garrett, and J.K. Alderfer. 1995. White-crowned Sparrow subspecies: identification and distribution. Birding 27(3):182-200.

Fish-n-Map Co. undated. Pacific Coast Charts. Map of offshore topography, Pt. Arguello to Mexico.

Franzreb, K.E. 1987. Endangered status and strategies for conservation of the Least Bell's Vireo (*Vireo bellii pusillus*). Western Birds 18:43-49.

----- 1989. Ecology and conservation of the endangered Least Bell's Vireo. Biological Report No. 89. U.S. Fish and Wildlife Service. Washington, D.C.

Frey, H.W., R.F. Hein, and J.L. Spruill. 1970. Report on the natural resources of Upper Newport Bay and recommendations concerning the Bay's development. Calif. Dept. of Fish & Game, Sacramento.

Gallagher, S., editor. 1993 (in prep.). Draft manuscript of The Orange County Breeding Bird Atlas. Scheduled to be published in 1996 or 1997 by Sea & Sage Press, Sea & Sage Audubon Society, Santa Ana.

Gardner, L.L. 1914. Additional notes on the birds of Laguna Beach. Journal of Entomology & Zoology (Pomona College) 6:235-239.

----- 1915. Notes from the sea coast of southern California. Condor 17:99.

Garrett, K.L., and J. Dunn. 1981. Birds of Southern California: Status and Distribution. Los Angeles Audubon Society. Los Angeles.

Garrett, K.L., editor. 1993. The biota of the Los Angeles River. Report, dated March 1993, prepared for the Calif. Dept. of Fish and Game by the Natural History Museum of Los Angeles County.

Gazzaniga, K.T. 1995. Distribution and dispersal of Black Skimmers (*Rynchops niger*) in southern California. M.S. Thesis, Calif. State Univ., Long Beach.

-----. 1996. Overwintering of Black Skimmers in California: site fidelity and inter-site movements. Western Birds 27(3):136-142.

Grinnell, J. 1898. Birds of the Pacific slope of Los Angeles County. Pasadena Academy of Sciences Publication No. 2.

----- 1909a. A bibliography of California Ornithology. Pacific Coast Avifauna No. 5.

----- 1909b. The Little Brown Crane in California. Condor 11:128-129.

----- 1924. A bibliography of California ornithology. Pacific Coast Avifauna No. 16.

----- 1939. A bibliography of California ornithology. Pacific Coast Avifauna No. 26.

Grinnell, J., H.C. Bryant, and T.I. Storer. 1918. The Game Birds of California. Univ. of Calif. Press, Berkeley.

Grinnell, J., and A.H. Miller. 1944. The distribution of the birds of California. Pacific Coast Avifauna No. 27.

Hall, E.R. 1981. The Mammals of North America. Second edition. John Wiley & Sons, New York, Chinchester, Brisbane, Toronto.

Hamilton, R.A. 1995. Photo quiz. Birding 27:298-301.

-----. 1996. Photo quiz. Birding 28(4):309-313.

Heindel, M.T., and M.A. Patten. 1996. Eighteenth report of the California Bird Records Committee: 1992 Records. Western Birds 27:1-29.

Hetrick, W., and R.G. McCaskie. 1965. Unusual behavior of a White-tailed Tropicbird in California. Condor 67:186-187.

Hickman, J.C. 1993. The Jepson Manual: Higher Plants of California. Univ. of Calif. Press, Berkeley.

Hoechlin, D. 1978. Yellow-crowned Night-Heron in California. Western Birds 9:177-178.

Howard, H. 1949. Avian fossils from the marine Pleistocene of southern California. Condor 51:20-28.

----- 1955. New records and a new species of Chendytes, an extinct genus of diving geese. Condor 57:135-143.

----- 1958. Further records from the Pleistocene of Newport Bay Mesa, California. Condor 60:136.

Huey, L.M. 1930. Comment on the marsh sparrows of southern and lower California, with the description of a new race. Transactions of the San Diego Society of Natural History 6:203-206.

Hutchinson, A.E., and M.C. Hutchinson. 1947. Breeding bird census: mature stand of live oaks along canyon creek. Audubon Field Notes 1:201.

Jehl, J.P. Jr. 1985. Hybridization and evolution of oystercatchers on the Pacific coast of Baja California. Ornithological Monographs 36:484-504.

Jehl, J.P. Jr., and N.K. Johnson (eds.). 1994. A century of avifaunal change in western North America. Studies in Avian Biology No. 15.

Johnson, J.W. 1990. The flora and fauna of Upper Newport Bay, 1940-55. Memoirs of the Natural History Foundation of Orange County 3:1-9.

Johnson, N.K. 1994. Pioneering and natural expansion of breeding distributions in western North American birds. Pp. 27-44 in J.R. Jehl, Jr., and N.K. Johnson (eds.), A century of avifaunal change in western North America. Studies in Avian Biology No. 15.

Johnston, R.F., and K.L. Garrett. 1994. Population trends of introduced birds in western North America. Pp. 221-231 in J.R. Jehl, Jr., and N.K. Johnson (eds.), A century of avifaunal change in western North America. Studies in Avian Biology No. 15.

Kingery, H.E. 1962. Breeding bird census: coastal chaparral. Audubon Field Notes 16:534-535.

Koford, C.B. 1966. The California Condor. Dover Publishing, New York.

Landry, R.E. 1974. Breeding bird census: urban, residential. American Birds 28:1054.

Laymon, S.A. 1987. Brown-headed Cowbirds in California: historical perspectives and management opportunities in riparian habitats. Western Birds 18:63-70.

Lee, E.K. 1973. Newport Bay, A Pioneer History. Newport Beach Historical Society, Sultana Press, Fullerton.

Lehman, P.E. 1994. The Birds of Santa Barbara County, California. Univ. of Calif. Santa Barbara Vertebrate Museum.

Lewis, J.C., K.L. Sallee, and R.T. Golightly, Jr. 1993. Introduced Red Fox in California. Report to Calif. Dept. of Fish & Game, Sacramento.

Linsdale, J.M. 1928. Variations in the Fox Sparrow (Passerella iliaca) with reference to natural history and osteology. Univ. of Calif. Publications in Zoology 30:251-392.

Marsh, G.A. 1992. Plants and Animals of the Santa Ana River in Orange County. Report dated July 1992, prepared for the County of Orange Environmental Management Agency/Public Works/Santa Ana River Project/Flood Control District, Santa Ana.

Massey, B.W. 1974. Breeding biology of the California Least Tern. Linnaean Society of New York, Proceedings 72:1-24.

McCaskie, R.G. 1964. Three southern herons in California. Condor 66:442-443.

----- 1965. The Cattle Egret reaches the west coast of the U.S. Condor 67:89.

----- 1967. The distribution of certain Mimidae in California. Condor. 69:310-311.

----- 1970. The Blackpoll Warbler in California. California Birds 1:95-104.

----- 1971. Rusty Blackbirds in California and western North America. California Birds 2:55-68.

McCaskie, R.G., R. Stallcup, and P. DeBenedictis. 1967a. The occurrence of certain flycatchers in California. Condor 69:85-86.

----- 1967b. The status of certain Fringillids in California. Condor 69:426-429.

McCrary, M., and P.H. Bloom. 1974. Breeding bird census: disturbed foothill grassland. American Birds 28:1043.

McKinnie, I.R., Jr. 1974. Breeding bird census: Sycamore-Coast Live Oak riparian woodland. American Birds 28:1036.

Miller, A.H. 1951. An analysis of the distribution of the birds of California. Univ. of Calif. Publications in Zoology 50:531-644.

Miller, L. 1918. The Eastern Kingbird in California again. Condor 20:44-45.

----- 1940. Observations on the Black-footed Albatross. Condor 42:229-238.

Mlodinow, S. 1993. Finding the Pacific Golden-Plover (*Pluvialis fulva*) in North America. Birding 25:322-329.

Monson, G., and A.R. Phillips. 1981. Annotated Checklist of the Birds of Arizona. Second edition. Univ. of Arizona Press. Tucson.

Osburn, P.I. 1911. The Yellow Rail in southern California. Condor 13:108.

Page, G.W., and L.E. Stenzel. 1981. The breeding status of the Snowy Plover in California. Western Birds 12:1-40.

Page, G.W., F.C. Bidstrup, R.J. Ramer, and L.E. Stenzel. 1986. Distribution of wintering Snowy Plovers in California and adjacent states. Western Birds 17:145-170.

Patten, M.A., and K.F. Campbell. 1994. Late nesting of the California Gnat-catcher. Western Birds 25:110-111.

Patten, M.A., and C.A. Marantz. 1996. Implications of vagrant southeastern vireos and warblers in California. Auk 113:911-923.

Patten, M.A., S.E. Finnegan, and P.E. Lehman. 1995. Seventeenth report of the California Bird Records Committee: 1991 records. Western Birds 26:113-143.

Pequegnat, W.E. 1951. The Biota of the Santa Ana Mountains. Journal of Entomology & Zoology (Pomona College) Vol. 42 Nos. 3, 4.

Pierce, W.M. 1919. Arctic Tern in Laguna Beach, California. Condor 21:125.

Pugh, E.A. 1955. Breeding bird census: brushy foothill. Audubon Field Notes 9:424.

----- 1956a. Breeding bird census: brushy foothill. Audubon Field Notes 10:428.

----- 1956b. Breeding bird census: sycamore-live oak dry wash. Audubon Field Notes 10:434-435.

----- 1964. Breeding bird census: brushy coastal bluff. Audubon Field Notes 18:561-562.

----- 1966. Cedar Waxwing nesting in southern California. Condor 68:307-308.

Pyle, P., N. Nur, and D.F. DeSante. 1994. Trends in nocturnal migrant landbird populations at Southeast Farallon Island, California, 1968-1992. Pp. 58-74 in J.R. Jehl, Jr., and N.K. Johnson (eds.), A century of avifaunal change in western North America. Studies in Avian Biology No. 15.

Pyle, R.L., and A. Small. 1961. Birds of Southern California: Annotated Field List. Otis Wade, Los Angeles.

Rakestraw, J. 1996. Keeping field notes. Birding 28:53-55.

Rea, A.M., and K.L. Weaver. 1990. The taxonomy, distribution, and status of coastal California Cactus Wrens. Western Birds 21:81-126.

Rising, J. 1996. A Guide to the Identification and Natural History of the Sparrows of the United States and Canada. Academic Press, San Diego, California.

Robbins, C.S. 1973. Introduction, spread and present abundance of the House Sparrow in North America. Ornithological Monographs 14:3-9.

Roberts, F.M., Jr. 1989. A Checklist of the Vascular Plants of Orange County, California. Univ. of Calif. Irvine Museum of Systematic Biology. Research Series No. 6.

Robertson, J.McB. 1910. Notes on Swainson's Hawks. Bird-Lore 12:147.

----- 1921. Southern California Screech Owls in western Orange County. Condor 23:97-98.

----- 1924. English Sparrow at Buena Park, Orange County. Condor 26:105-106.

----- 1925. Further notes on Screech Owls at Buena Park. Condor 27:35-36.

----- 1927. Lark Bunting in Orange County, California. Condor 29:203.

----- 1929. The White-tailed Kite in Orange County, California. Condor 31:181.

----- 1930. Migratory flight of Swainson's Hawks. Condor 32:127.

----- 1931a. Birds and eucalyptus trees. Condor 33:137-139.

----- 1931b. Some changes in the bird life of western Orange County, California. Condor 33:204-205.

----- 1932. Slight expansion of breeding range of Barn Swallows in Orange County, California. Condor 34:259.

----- 1933. White-crowned Sparrow records from southern California. Condor 35:164.

----- 1938. Harris' Sparrow at Buena Park, California. Condor 40:186.

Romero, P.D. 1971. Anaheim Bay Study, July 1970-June 1971. Calif. Dept. Fish & Game Special Wildlife Investigative Report.

Ross, R.C. 1925. Western martin colonies. Condor 27:209.

Rothstein. S.I. 1994. The cowbird's invasion of the far west: history, causes and consequences experienced by host species. Pp. 301-315 in Jehl, J.P. Jr., and N.K. Johnson (eds.), A century of avifaunal change in western North America. Studies in Avian Biology No. 15.

Rowley, J.S. 1930. Observations on the Dwarf Cowbird. Condor 32:130-131.

Schaffner, F.C. 1985. Royal Tern nesting attempts in California: isolated or significant incidents? Western Birds 16:71-80.

Schneider, F.B. 1927. Invasion of southern California coast by Elegant Terns. Condor 29:71.

Schneider, J.J. 1900a. Nesting of the Pileated Warbler in Los Angeles County. Condor 2:33.

----- 1900b. Nesting of the California Cuckoo in Los Angeles County. Condor 2:34.

Sexton, C.W. 1972a. Avian use of Upper Newport Bay and other parts of the estuary/lagoon ecosystem of southern California. Dept. of Population and Environmental Biology, Univ. of Calif. Irvine.

----- 1972b. Clapper Rails at Upper Newport Bay, California. Dept. of Population and Environmental Biology, Univ. of Calif. Irvine.

Sexton, C.W., and G.L. Hunt. 1979. An annotated checklist of the birds of Orange County, California. Univ. of Calif. Irvine Museum of Systematic Biology Research Series No. 5.

Sharp, C.S. 1907. The breeding birds of Escondido. Condor 9:84-88.

Shepardson, D.I. 1909. Notes on the nesting of the Bank Swallow. Condor 11:174.

Short, L.L. Jr. 1971. Systematics and behavior of some North American woodpeckers, genus Picoides (Aves). Bulletin of the American Museum of Natural History 145:1-118.

Sibley, D. 1996. Field identification of the Sharp-tailed Sparrow complex. Birding 28:196-208.

Skinner, M.P. 1933. White-throated Swifts at San Juan Capistrano. Condor 35:241.

Sleeper, J.D. 1973. Turn the Rascals Out! California Classics, Trabuco Canyon, Calif.

----- 1986. Jim Sleeper's 3rd Orange County Almanac of Historical Oddities. Sultana Press, Fullerton, Calif.

Smice, R.E. 1974. Breeding bird census: coastal sage scrub. American Birds 28:1042.

Springer, P.F. 1990. Identification of Aleutian Canada Goose (Branta canadensis leucopareia). Two-page handout on file at Sea & Sage Audubon House, Irvine.

Springer, P.F., and R.B McNab. 1990. Field notes on subspecies of Canada Geese (Branta canadensis) occurring in California. Two-page handout on file at Sea & Sage Audubon House, Irvine.

Stepniewski, A. 1971. Birds of the San Joaquin Marsh. Dept. of Population and Environmental Biology, Univ. of Calif. Irvine.

Storer, T.R., and L.P. Tevis, Jr. 1955. California Grizzly. Univ. of Nebraska Press, Lincoln.

Swarth, H.S. (1908). Santa Ana Mountains area, southern California, Sept. 9-23, 1908. Pp. 116-132 of unpublished field notes. Museum of Vertebrate Biology, Univ. of Calif. Berkeley; copy on file at Sea & Sage Audubon House, Irvine.

----- 1920. Revision of the avian genus Passerella, with special reference to the distribution and migration of the races in California. Univ. of Calif. Publications in Zoology 21:75-224.

Takekawa, J.E., H.R. Carter, and T.E. Harvey. 1990. Decline of the Common Murre in central California, 1980-1986. Pp. 149-163 *in* S.G. Sealy (ed.), Auks at sea. Studies in Avian Biology No. 14.

Talbert, T.B. 1982. My Sixty Years in California. Ben Franklin Press, Huntington Beach, Calif.

Terrill, S., K.P. Able, and M.A. Patten. 1992. The changing seasons: Summer 1992. American Birds 47:1109-1111 and 1182.

Thelander, C.G., and M. Crabtree, editors. 1994. Life on the Edge: A Guide to California's Endangered Natural Resources: Wildlife. Biosystems Books, Santa Cruz, Calif.

Todd, F.S. 1979. Waterfowl: Ducks, Geese, and Swans of the World. Seaworld, San Diego, Calif.

Unitt, P. 1984. The birds of San Diego County. San Diego Society of Natural History Memoir No. 13.

----- 1987. *Empidonax traillii extimus*: an endangered subspecies. Western Birds 18(3):137-162.

Unitt, P., K. Messer, and M. Thery. 1996. Taxonomy of the Marsh Wren in southern California. Proceedings of the San Diego Natural History Museum No. 31.

Van Tyne, J. 1956. What constitutes scientific data for the study of bird distribution? Wilson Bulletin 68:63-67.

----- 1965. What constitutes scientific data for the study of bird distribution? (revised) Audubon Field Notes 19:390-392.

van Rossem, A.J. 1922a. Possible occurrence of the Blue-footed Booby in southern California. Condor 24:28.

----- 1922b. The Salt Marsh Yellowthroat in Southern California. Condor 24:134.

Webster, R.E. 1993. Building a birder's library. Birding 25:10-45.

Wells, S., and L.F. Baptista. 1978. Breeding of Allen's Hummingbird (*Selasphorus sasin sedentarius*) on the southern California mainland. Western Birds 10:83-85.

Wilbur, S.R., W.P. Carrier, and R.G. McCaskie. 1971. The Lark Bunting in California. California Birds 2(2):73-76.

Willett, G. 1910. Southern California breeding records of the Western Grasshopper Sparrow. Condor 12:204.

----- 1912. Birds of the Pacific slope of southern California. Pacific Coast Avifauna No. 7.

----- 1930. Least Bittern in California in winter. Condor 32:64.

----- 1933. Revised list of the birds of southwestern California. Pacific Coast Avifauna No. 21.

Willick, D.R., and M.A. Patten. 1992. Finding the California Gnatcatcher in the U.S. Birding 24:234-239.

Woodbury, A.M., and H. Knight. 1951. Results of the Pacific gull color-banding project. Condor 53:57-77.

Wyman, L.E. 1917. Fork-tailed Petrel and Baird Sandpiper in southern California. Condor 19:141-142.

Zembal, R. 1992. Status and management of Light-footed Clapper Rails in coastal southern California. Transactions of the Western Section of the Wildlife Society 28:1-5.

----- 1993. Light-footed Clapper Rail management and population assessment. Calif. Dept. of Fish & Game Non-game Bird and Mammal Program Report No. 94-6. Sacramento.

Zembal, R., and B.W. Massey. 1981. A census of the Light-footed Clapper Rail in California. Western Birds 12:87-99.

Zembal, R., K.J. Kramer, R.J. Bransfield, and N. Gilbert. 1988. A survey of Belding's Savannah Sparrow in California. American Birds 42:1233-1236.

Zembal, R., G.P. Wheeler, and D.A. Pierce. 1982. Breeding bird census: creekside willow woodland. American Birds 36:87-88.

Zink, R.M. 1994. The geography of mitochondrial DNA variation, population structure, hybridization, and species limits in the Fox Sparrow (*Passerella iliaca*). Evolution 48:96-111.

Index of Common Bird Names

This index covers the bar graphs, annotations, supplemental list, and introduced/exotic species section.

Appendix A - Checklist

	1	2	3	4	5	6	7	8	9	10
Loons - Gaviidae										
Red-throated Loon *Gavia stellata*										
Pacific Loon *Gavia pacifica*										
Common Loon *Gavia immer*										
Grebes - Podicipedidae										
Pied-billed Grebe *Podilymbus podiceps*										
Horned Grebe *Podiceps auritus*										
Red-necked Grebe *Podiceps grisegena*										
Eared Grebe *Podiceps nigricollis*										
Western Grebe *Aechmophorus occidentalis*										
Clark's Grebe *Aechmophorus clarkii*										
Albatrosses - Diomedeidae										
Short-tailed Albatross *Diomedea albatrus*										
Black-footed Albatross *Diomedea nigripes*										
Shearwaters and Petrels - Procellariidae										
Northern Fulmar *Fulmaris glacialis*										
Pink-footed Shearwater *Puffinus creatopus*										
Flesh-footed Shearwater *Puffinus carneipes*										
Buller's Shearwater *Puffinus bulleri*										
Sooty Shearwater *Puffinus griseus*										
Short-tailed Shearwater *Puffinus tenuirostris*										
Black-vented Shearwater *Puffinus opisthomelas*										
Storm-Petrels - Hydrobatidae										
Wilson's Storm-Petrel *Oceanites oceanicus*										
Fork-tailed Storm-Petrel *Oceanodroma furcata*										
Ashy Storm-Petrel *Oceanodroma homochroa*										
Black Storm-Petrel *Oceanodroma melania*										
Least Storm-Petrel *Oceanodroma microsoma*										
Tropicbirds - Phaethontidae										
White-tailed Tropicbird *Phaethon lepturus*										
Red-billed Tropicbird *Pheathon aethereus*										
Boobies and Gannets - Sulidae										
Masked Booby *Sula dactylatra*										
Blue-footed Booby *Sula nebouxii*										
Pelicans - Pelecanidae										
American White Pelican *Pelecanus erythrorhynchos*										
Brown Pelican *Pelecanus occidentalis*										
Cormorants - Phalacrocoracidae										
Double-crested Cormorant *Phlacrocorax auritus*										
Brandt's Cormorant *Phalacrocorax penicillatus*										
Pelagic Cormorant *Phalacrocorax pelagicus*										
Frigatebirds - Fregatidae										
Magnificent Frigatebird *Fregata magnificens*										

	1	2	3	4	5	6	7	8	9	10
Bitterns and Herons - Ardeidae										
American Bittern *Botaurus lentiginosus*										
Least Bittern *Ixobrychus exilis*										
Great Blue Heron *Ardea herodias*										
Great Egret *Ardea alba*										
Snowy Egret *Egretta thula*										
Little Blue Heron *Egretta caerulea*										
Tricolored Heron *Egretta tricolor*										
Reddish Egret *Egretta rufescens*										
Cattle Egret *Bubulcus ibis*										
Green Heron *Butorides virescens*										
Black-crowned Night-Heron *Nycticorax nycticorax*										
Yellow-crowned Night-Heron *Nyctanassa violacea*										
Ibises and Spoonbills - Threskiornithidae										
White-faced Ibis *Plegadis chihi*										
Roseate Spoonbill *Ajaia ajaja*										
Storks - Ciconiidae										
Wood Stork *Mycteria americana*										
Swans, Geese and Ducks - Anatidae										
Fulvous Whistling-Duck *Dendrocygna bicolor*										
Tundra Swan *Cygnus columbianus*										
Greater White-fronted Goose *Anser albifrons*										
Snow Goose *Chen caerulescens*										
Ross' Goose *Chen rossii*										
Emperor Goose *Chen canagica*										
Brant *Branta bernicla*										
Canada Goose *Branta canadensis*										
"Western" *B.c. moffitti*										
"Taverner's" *B.c. taverneri*										
"Aleutian" *B.c. leucopareia*										
"Cackling" *B.c. minima*										
Wood Duck *Aix sponsa*										
Green-winged Teal *Anas crecca*										
"Eurasian" *A.c. crecca*										
"American" *A.c. carolinensis*										
Mallard *Anas platyrhynchos*										
Northern Pintail *Anas acuta*										
Garganey *Anas querquedula*										
Blue-winged Teal *Anas discors*										
Cinnamon Teal *Anas cyanoptera*										
Northern Shoveler *Anas clypeata*										
Gadwall *Anas strepera*										
Eurasian Wigeon *Anas penelope*										
American Wigeon *Anas americana*										
Canvasback *Aythya valisineria*										

	1	2	3	4	5	6	7	8	9	10
Redhead *Aythya americana*										
Ring-necked Duck *Aythya collaris*										
Greater Scaup *Aythya marila*										
Lesser Scaup *Aythya affinis*										
King Eider *Somateria spectabilis*										
Harlequin Duck *Histrionicus histrionicus*										
Oldsquaw *Clangula hyemalis*										
Black Scoter *Melanitta nigra*										
Surf Scoter *Melanitta perspicillata*										
White-winged Scoter *Melanitta fusca*										
Common Goldeneye *Bucephala clangula*										
Barrow's Goldeneye *Bucephala islandica*										
Bufflehead *Bucephala albeola*										
Hooded Merganser *Lophodytes cucullatus*										
Common Merganser *Mergus merganser*										
Red-breasted Merganser *Mergus serrator*										
Ruddy Duck *Oxyura jamaicensis*										
American Vultures - Cathartidae										
Turkey Vulture *Cathartes aura*										
California Condor *Gymnogyps californianus*										
Kites, Hawks, Eagles and Allies - Accipitridae										
Osprey *Pandion haliaetus*										
White-tailed Kite *Elanus leucurus*										
Mississippi Kite *Ictinia mississippiensis*										
Bald Eagle *Haliaeetus leucocephalus*										
Northern Harrier *Circus cyaneus*										
Sharp-shinned Hawk *Accipiter striatus*										
Cooper's Hawk *Accipiter cooperii*										
Red-shouldered Hawk *Buteo lineatus*										
Broad-winged Hawk *Buteo platypterus*										
Swainson's Hawk *Buteo swainsoni*										
Zone-tailed Hawk *Buteo albonotatus*										
Red-tailed Hawk *Buteo jamaicensis*										
"Western" *B.j. calurus*										
"Harlan's" *B.j. harlani*										
Ferruginous Hawk *Buteo regalis*										
Rough-legged Hawk *Buteo lagopus*										
Golden Eagle *Aquila chrysaetos*										
Falcons - Falconidae										
American Kestrel *Falco sparverius*										
Merlin *Falco columbarius*										
"Taiga" *F.c. columbarius/bendirei*										
"Black" *F.c. suckleyi*										
"Prairie" *F.c. richardsonii*										
Peregrine Falcon *Falco peregrinus*										

	1	2	3	4	5	6	7	8	9	10
Prairie Falcon *Falco mexicanus*										
Partridges, Grouse, Turkeys and Quail - Phasianidae										
California Quail *Callipepla californica*										
Mountain Quail *Oreortyx pictus*										
Rails, Gallinules and Coots - Rallidae										
Yellow Rail *Coturnicops noveboracensis*										
Black Rail *Laterallus jamaicensis*										
Clapper Rail *Rallus longirostris*										
Virginia Rail *Rallus limicola*										
Sora *Porzana carolina*										
Common Moorhen *Gallinula chloropus*										
American Coot *Fulica americana*										
Cranes - Gruidae										
Sandhill Crane *Grus canadensis*										
Plovers - Charadriidae										
Black-bellied Plover *Pluvialis squatarola*										
American Golden-Plover *Pluvialis dominicus*										
Pacific Golden-Plover *Pluvialis fulva*										
Snowy Plover *Charadrius alexandrinus*										
Semipalmated Plover *Charadrius semipalmatus*										
Killdeer *Charadrius vociferus*										
Mountain Plover *Charadrius montanus*										
Oystercatchers - Haematopodidae										
American Oystercatcher *Haematopus palliatus*										
Black Oystercatcher *Haematopus bachmani*										
Stilts and Avocets - Recurvirostridae										
Black-necked Stilt *Himantopus mexicanus*										
American Avocet *Recurvirostra americana*										
Sandpipers, Phalaropes and Allies - Scolopacidae										
Greater Yellowlegs *Tringa melanoleuca*										
Lesser Yellowlegs *Tringa flavipes*										
Solitary Sandpiper *Tringa solitaria*										
Willet *Catoptrophorus semipalmatus*										
Wandering Tattler *Heteroscelus incanus*										
Spotted Sandpiper *Actitis macularia*										
Whimbrel *Numenius phaeopus*										
Long-billed Curlew *Numenius americanus*										
Marbled Godwit *Limosa fedoa*										
Ruddy Turnstone *Arenaria interpres*										
Black Turnstone *Arenaria melanocephala*										
Surfbird *Aphriza virgata*										
Red Knot *Calidris canutus*										
Sanderling *Calidris alba*										
Semipalmated Sandpiper *Calidris pusilla*										
Western Sandpiper *Calidris mauri*										

	1	2	3	4	5	6	7	8	9	10
Little Stint *Calidris minuta*										
Least Sandpiper *Calidris minutilla*										
White-rumped Sandpiper *Calidris fuscicollis*										
Baird's Sandpiper *Calidris bairdii*										
Pectoral Sandpiper *Calidris melanotos*										
Sharp-tailed Sandpiper *Calidris acuminata*										
Dunlin *Calidris alpina*										
Curlew Sandpiper *Calidris ferruginea*										
Stilt Sandpiper *Calidris himantopus*										
Ruff *Philomachus pugnax*										
Short-billed Dowitcher *Limnodromus griseus*										
Long-billed Dowitcher *Limnodromus scolopaceus*										
Common Snipe *Gallinago gallinago*										
Wilson's Phalarope *Phalaropus tricolor*										
Red-necked Phalarope *Phalaropus lobatus*										
Red Phalarope *Phalaropus fulicaria*										
Skuas, Gulls, Terns and Skimmers - Laridae										
Pomarine Jaeger *Stercorarius pomarinus*										
Parasitic Jaeger *Stercorarius parasiticus*										
Long-tailed Jaeger *Stercorarius longicaudus*										
South Polar Skua *Catharacta maccormicki*										
Laughing Gull *Larus atricilla*										
Franklin's Gull *Larus pipixcan*										
Little Gull *Larus minutus*										
Black-headed Gull *Larus ridibundus*										
Bonaparte's Gull *Larus philadelphia*										
Heermann's Gull *Larus heermanni*										
Mew Gull *Larus canus*										
Ring-billed Gull *Larus delawarensis*										
California Gull *Larus californicus*										
Herring Gull *Larus argentatus*										
Thayer's Gull *Larus thayeri*										
Lesser Black-backed Gull *Larus fuscus*										
Yellow-footed Gull *Larus livens*										
Western Gull *Larus occidentalis*										
"Northern" *L.o. occidentalis*										
"Southern" *L.o. wymani*										
Glaucous-winged Gull *Larus glaucescens*										
Glaucous Gull *Larus hyperboreus*										
Black-legged Kittiwake *Rissa tridactyla*										
Sabine's Gull *Xema sabini*										
Ivory Gull *Pagophila eburnea*										
Gull-billed Tern *Gelochelidon nilotica*										
Caspian Tern *Sterna caspia*										
Royal Tern *Sterna maxima*										

	1	2	3	4	5	6	7	8	9	10
Elegant Tern *Sterna elegans*										
Sandwich Tern *Sterna sandvicensis*										
Common Tern *Sterna hirundo*										
Arctic Tern *Sterna paradisaea*										
Forster's Tern *Sterna forsteri*										
Least Tern *Sterna antillarum*										
Sooty Tern *Sterna fuscata*										
Black Tern *Chlidonias niger*										
Black Skimmer *Rynchops niger*										
Auks, Murres and Puffins - Alcidae										
Common Murre *Uria aalge*										
Pigeon Guillemot *Cepphus columba*										
Xantus' Murrelet *Synthliboramphus hypoleucus*										
Craveri's Murrelet *Synthliboramphus craveri*										
Ancient Murrelet *Synthliboramphus antiquus*										
Cassin's Auklet *Ptychoramphus aleuticus*										
Rhinoceros Auklet *Cerorhinca monocerata*										
Horned Puffin *Fratercula corniculata*										
Pigeons and Doves - Columbidae										
Band-tailed Pigeon *Columba fasciata*										
White-winged Dove *Zenaida asiatica*										
Mourning Dove *Zenaida macroura*										
Common Ground-Dove *Colmbina passerina*										
Ruddy Ground-Dove *Columbina talpacoti*										
Cuckoos, Roadrunners and Anis - Cuculidae										
Black-billed Cuckoo *Coccyzus erythropthalmus*										
Yellow-billed Cuckoo *Coccyzus americanus*										
Greater Roadrunner *Geococcyx californianus*										
Groove-billed Ani *Crotophaga sulcirostris*										
Barn Owls - Tytonidae										
Barn Owl *Tyto alba*										
Typical Owls - Strigidae										
Western Screech-Owl *Otus kennicottii*										
Great Horned Owl *Bubo virginianus*										
Burrowing Owl *Speotyto cunicularia*										
Spotted Owl *Strix occidentalis*										
Long-eared Owl *Asio otus*										
Short-eared Owl *Asio flammeus*										
Northern Saw-whet Owl *Aegolius acadicus*										
Goatsuckers - Caprimulgidae										
Lesser Nighthawk *Chordeiles acutipennis*										
Common Nighthawk *Chordeiles minor*										
Common Poorwill *Phalaenoptilus nuttallii*										

	1	2	3	4	5	6	7	8	9	10
Swifts - Apodidae										
Black Swift *Cypseloides niger*										
Chimney Swift *Chaetura pelagica*										
Vaux's Swift *Chaetura vauxi*										
White-throated Swift *Aeronautes saxatalis*										
Hummingbirds - Trochilidae										
Broad-billed Hummingbird *Cynanthus latirostris*										
Black-chinned Hummingbird *Archilochus alexandri*										
Anna's Hummingbird *Calypte anna*										
Costa's Hummingbird *Calypte costae*										
Calliope Hummingbird *Stellula calliope*										
Rufous Hummingbird *Selasphorus rufus*										
Allen's Hummingbird *Selasphorus sasin*										
Kingfishers - Alcedinidae										
Belted Kingfisher *Ceryle alcyon*										
Woodpeckers - Picidae										
Lewis' Woodpecker *Melanerpes lewis*										
Acorn Woodpecker *Melanerpes formicivorus*										
Yellow-bellied Sapsucker *Sphyrapicus varius*										
Red-naped Sapsucker *Sphyrapicus nuchalis*										
Red-breasted Sapsucker *Sphyrapicus ruber*										
Williamson's Sapsucker *Sphyrapicus thyroideus*										
Nuttall's Woodpecker *Picoides nuttallii*										
Downy Woodpecker *Picoides pubescens*										
Hairy Woodpecker *Picoides villosus*										
White-headed Woodpecker *Picoides albolarvatus*										
Northern Flicker *Colaptes auratus*										
"Yellow-shafted" *auritus* group										
"Red-shafted" *cafer* group										
Tyrant Flycatchers - Tyrannidae										
Olive-sided Flycatcher *Contopus borealis*										
Greater Pewee *Contopus pertinax*										
Western Wood-Pewee *Contopus sordidulus*										
Willow Flycatcher *Empidonax traillii*										
Least Flycatcher *Empidonax minimus*										
Hammond's Flycatcher *Empidonax hammondii*										
Dusky Flycatcher *Empidonax oberholseri*										
Gray Flycatcher *Empidonax wrightii*										
Pacific-slope Flycatcher *Empidonax difficilis*										
Black Phoebe *Sayornis nigricans*										
Eastern Phoebe *Sayornis phoebe*										
Say's Phoebe *Sayornis saya*										
Vermilion Flycatcher *Pyrocephalus rubinus*										
Dusky-capped Flycatcher *Myiarchus tuberculifer*										
Ash-throated Flycatcher *Myiarchus cinerascens*										

	1	2	3	4	5	6	7	8	9	10
Great Crested Flycatcher *Myiarchus crinitus*										
Brown-crested Flycatcher *Myiarchus tyrannulus*										
Sulphur-bellied Flycatcher *Myiodynastes luteiventris*										
Tropical Kingbird *Tyrannus melancholicus*										
Cassin's Kingbird *Tyrannus vociferans*										
Thick-billed Kingbird *Tyrannus crassirostris*										
Western Kingbird *Tyrannus verticalis*										
Eastern Kingbird *Tyrannus tyrannus*										
Scissor-tailed Flycatcher *Tyrannus forficatus*										
Larks - Alaudidae										
Horned Lark *Eremophila alpestris*										
Swallows - Hirundinidae										
Purple Martin *Progne subis*										
Tree Swallow *Tachycineta bicolor*										
Violet-green Swallow *Tachycineta thalassina*										
Northern Rough-winged Swallow *Stelgidopteryx serripennis*										
Bank Swallow *Riparia riparia*										
Cliff Swallow *Hirundo pyrrhonota*										
Barn Swallow *Hirundo rustica*										
Jays, Magpies and Crows - Corvidae										
Steller's Jay *Cyanocitta stelleri*										
Western Scrub-Jay *Aphelocoma californica*										
Clark's Nutcracker *Nucifraga columbiana*										
American Crow *Corvus brachyrhynchos*										
Common Raven *Corvus corax*										
Titmice - Paridae										
Mountain Chickadee *Parus gambeli*										
Plain Titmouse *Parus inornatus*										
Bushtits - Aegithalidae										
Bushtit *Psaltriparus minimus*										
Nuthatches - Sittidae										
Red-breasted Nuthatch *Sitta canadensis*										
White-breasted Nuthatch *Sitta carolinensis*										
Pygmy Nuthatch *Sitta pygmaea*										
Creepers - Certhiidae										
Brown Creeper *Certhia americana*										
Wrens - Troglodytidae										
Cactus Wren *Campylorhynchus brunneicapillus*										
Rock Wren *Salpinctes obsoletus*										
Canyon Wren *Catherpes mexicanus*										
Bewick's Wren *Thryomanes bewickii*										
House Wren *Troglodytes aedon*										
Winter Wren *Troglodytes troglodytes*										
Sedge Wren *Cistothorus platensis*										
Marsh Wren *Cistothorus palustris*										

	1	2	3	4	5	6	7	8	9	10
Dippers - Cinclidae										
American Dipper *Cinclus mexicanus*										
Muscicapids - Muscicapidae										
Golden-crowned Kinglet *Regulus satrapa*										
Ruby-crowned Kinglet *Regulus calendula*										
Blue-gray Gnatcatcher *Polioptila caerulea*										
California Gnatcatcher *Polioptila californica*										
Western Bluebird *Sialia mexicana*										
Mountain Bluebird *Sialia currucoides*										
Townsend's Solitaire *Myadestes townsendi*										
Swainson's Thrush *Catharus ustulatus*										
Hermit Thrush *Catharus guttatus*										
Rufous-backed Robin *Turdus rufopalliatus*										
American Robin *Turdus migratorius*										
Varied Thrush *Ixoreus naevius*										
Wrentit *Chamaea fasciata*										
Mockingbirds and Thrashers - Mimidae										
Gray Catbird *Dumetella carolinensis*										
Northern Mockingbird *Mimus polyglottos*										
Sage Thrasher *Oreoscoptes montanus*										
Brown Thrasher *Toxostoma rufum*										
Bendire's Thrasher *Toxostoma bendirei*										
California Thrasher *Toxostoma redivivum*										
Wagtails and Pipits - Motacillidae										
Yellow Wagtail *Motacilla flava*										
Black-backed Wagtail *Motacilla lugens*										
Red-throated Pipit *Anthus cervinus*										
American Pipit *Anthus rubescens*										
Sprague's Pipit *Anthus spragueii*										
Waxwings - Bombycillidae										
Bohemian Waxwing *Bombycilla garrulus*										
Cedar Waxwing *Bombycilla cedrorum*										
Silky-Flycatchers - Ptilogonatidae										
Phainopepla *Phainopepla nitens*										
Shrikes - Laniidae										
Loggerhead Shrike *Lanius ludovicianus*										
Vireos - Vireonidae										
White-eyed Vireo *Vireo griseus*										
Bell's Vireo *Vireo bellii*										
"Eastern"/"Texas" *V.b. bellii/medius*										
"Least" *V.b. pusillus*										
Solitary Vireo *Vireo solitarius*										
"Blue-headed" *V.s. solitarius*										
"Plumbeous" *V.s. plumbeus*										
"Cassin's" *V.s. cassinii*										

	1	2	3	4	5	6	7	8	9	10
Yellow-throated Vireo *Vireo flavifrons*										
Hutton's Vireo *Vireo huttoni*										
Warbling Vireo *Vireo gilvus*										
Philadelphia Vireo *Vireo philadelphicus*										
Red-eyed Vireo *Vireo olivaceus*										
Yellow-green Vireo *Vireo flavoviridis*										
Emberizids - Emberizidae										
Blue-winged Warbler *Vermivora pinus*										
Golden-winged Warbler *Vermivora chrysoptera*										
Tennessee Warbler *Vermivora peregrina*										
Orange-crowned Warbler *Vermivora celata*										
"Eastern"/"Rocky Mountain" *V.c. celata/orestra*										
"Lutescent" *V.c. lutescens*										
"Dusky" *V.c. sordida*										
Nashville Warbler *Vermivora ruficapilla*										
Virginia's Warbler *Vermivora virginiae*										
Lucy's Warbler *Vermivora luciae*										
Northern Parula *Parula americana*										
Yellow Warbler *Dendroica petechia*										
Chestnut-sided Warbler *Dendroica pensylvanica*										
Magnolia Warbler *Dendroica magnolia*										
Cape May Warbler *Dendroica tigrina*										
Black-throated Blue Warbler *Dendroica caerulescens*										
Yellow-rumped Warbler *Dendroica coronata*										
"Myrtle" *D.c. coronata* group										
"Audubon's" *D.c. auduboni* group										
Black-throated Gray Warbler *Dendroica nigrescens*										
Townsend's Warbler *Dendroica townsendi*										
Hermit Warbler *Dendroica occidentalis*										
Black-throated Green Warbler *Dendroica virens*										
Blackburnian Warbler *Dendroica fusca*										
Grace's Warbler *Dendroica graciae*										
Pine Warbler *Dendroica pinus*										
Prairie Warbler *Dendroica discolor*										
Palm Warbler *Dendroica palmarum*										
Bay-breasted Warbler *Dendroica castanea*										
Blackpoll Warbler *Dendroica striata*										
Cerulean Warbler *Dendroica cerulea*										
Black-and-white Warbler *Mniotilta varia*										
American Redstart *Setophaga ruticilla*										
Prothonotary Warbler *Protonotaria citrea*										
Worm-eating Warbler *Helmitheros vermivorus*										
Ovenbird *Seiurus aurocapillus*										
Northern Waterthrush *Seiurus noveboracensis*										
Louisiana Waterthrush *Seiurus motacilla*										

	1	2	3	4	5	6	7	8	9	10
Kentucky Warbler *Oporornis formosus*										
Mourning Warbler *Oporornis philadelphia*										
MacGillivray's Warbler *Oporornis tolmiei*										
Common Yellowthroat *Geothlypis trichas*										
Hooded Warbler *Wilsonia citrina*										
Wilson's Warbler *Wilsonia pusilla*										
Canada Warbler *Wilsonia canadensis*										
Painted Redstart *Myioborus pictus*										
Yellow-breasted Chat *Icteria virens*										
Hepatic Tanager *Piranga flava*										
Summer Tanager *Piranga rubra*										
Scarlet Tanager *Piranga olivacea*										
Western Tanager *Piranga ludoviciana*										
Rose-breasted Grosbeak *Pheucticus ludovicianus*										
Black-headed Grosbeak *Pheucticus melanocephalus*										
Blue Grosbeak *Guiraca caerulea*										
Lazuli Bunting *Passerina amoena*										
Indigo Bunting *Passerina cyanea*										
Painted Bunting *Passerina ciris*										
Dickcissel *Spiza americana*										
Green-tailed Towhee *Pipilo chlorurus*										
Spotted Towhee *Pipilo maculatus*										
California Towhee *Pipilo crissalis*										
Cassin's Sparrow *Aimophila cassinii*										
Rufous-crowned Sparrow *Aimophila ruficeps*										
American Tree Sparrow *Spizella arborea*										
Chipping Sparrow *Spizella passerina*										
Clay-colored Sparrow *Spizella pallida*										
Brewer's Sparrow *Spizella breweri*										
Field Sparrow *Spizella pusilla*										
Black-chinned Sparrow *Spizella atrogularis*										
Vesper Sparrow *Pooecetes gramineus*										
Lark Sparrow *Chondestes grammacus*										
Black-throated Sparrow *Amphispiza bilineata*										
Sage Sparrow *Amphispiza belli*										
Lark Bunting *Calamospiza melanocorys*										
Savannah Sparrow *Passerculus sandwichensis*										
northern/interior subspecies										
"Belding's" *P.s. beldingi*										
"Large-billed" *P.s. rostratus*										
Grasshopper Sparrow *Ammodramus savannarum*										
Le Conte's Sparrow *Ammodramus leconteii*										
Nelson's Sharp-tailed Sparrow *Ammodramus nelsoni*										

	1	2	3	4	5	6	7	8	9	10
Fox Sparrow *Passerella iliaca*										
"Red" *iliaca* group										
"Sooty" *unalaschcensis* group										
"Slate-colored" *schistacea* group										
"Thick-billed" *megarhynchus* group										
Song Sparrow *Melospiza melodia*										
Lincoln's Sparrow *Melospiza lincolnii*										
Swamp Sparrow *Melospiza georgiana*										
White-throated Sparrow *Zonotrichia albicollis*										
Golden-crowned Sparrow *Zonotrichia atricapilla*										
White-crowned Sparrow *Zonotrichia leucophrys*										
"Gambel's" *Z.l. gambelii*										
"Mountain" *Z.l. oriantha*										
"Puget Sound" *Z.l. pugetensis*										
Harris' Sparrow *Zonotrichia querula*										
Dark-eyed Junco *Junco hyemalis*										
"Slate-colored" *hyemalis* group										
"Oregon" *oreganus* group										
"Pink-sided" *J.h. mearnsi*										
"Gray-headed" *caniceps* group										
McCown's Longspur *Calcarius mccownii*										
Lapland Longspur *Calcarius lapponicus*										
Chestnut-collared Longspur *Calcarius ornatus*										
Bobolink *Dolichonyx oryzivorus*										
Red-winged Blackbird *Agelaius phoeniceus*										
Tricolored Blackbird *Agelaius tricolor*										
Western Meadowlark *Sturnella neglecta*										
Yellow-headed Blackbird *Xanthocephalus xanthocephalus*										
Rusty Blackbird *Euphagus carolinus*										
Brewer's Blackbird *Euphagus cyanocephalus*										
Great-tailed Grackle *Quiscalus mexicanus*										
Brown-headed Cowbird *Molothrus ater*										
Orchard Oriole *Icterus spurius*										
Hooded Oriole *Icterus cucullatus*										
Baltimore Oriole *Icterus galbula*										
Bullock's Oriole *Icterus bullockii*										
Scott's Oriole *Icterus parisorum*										
Cardueline Finches - Fringillidae										
Purple Finch *Carpodacus purpureus*										
House Finch *Carpodacus mexicanus*										
Red Crossbill *Loxia curvirostra*										
Pine Siskin *Carduelis pinus*										
Lesser Goldfinch *Carduelis psaltria*										
Lawrence's Goldfinch *Carduelis lawrencei*										
American Goldfinch *Carduelis tristis*										

	1	2	3	4	5	6	7	8	9	10
Introduced Species										
Rock Dove *Columba livia*										
Spotted Dove *Streptopelia chinensis*										
European Starling *Sturnus vulgaris*										
House Sparrow *Passer domesticus*										

Checklist 1
Locality:
Date(s):
Remarks:

Checklist 6
Locality:
Date(s):
Remarks:

Checklist 2
Locality:
Date(s):
Remarks:

Checklist 7
Locality:
Date(s):
Remarks:

Checklist 3
Locality:
Date(s):
Remarks:

Checklist 8
Locality:
Date(s):
Remarks:

Checklist 4
Locality:
Date(s):
Remarks:

Checklist 9
Locality:
Date(s):
Remarks:

Checklist 5
Locality:
Date(s):
Remarks:

Checklist 10
Locality:
Date(s):
Remarks:

Appendix B - Maps

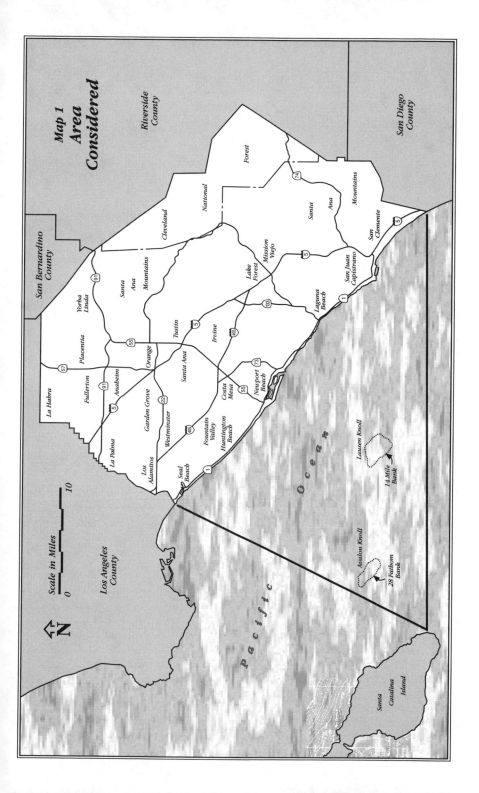

Map 1
Area Considered

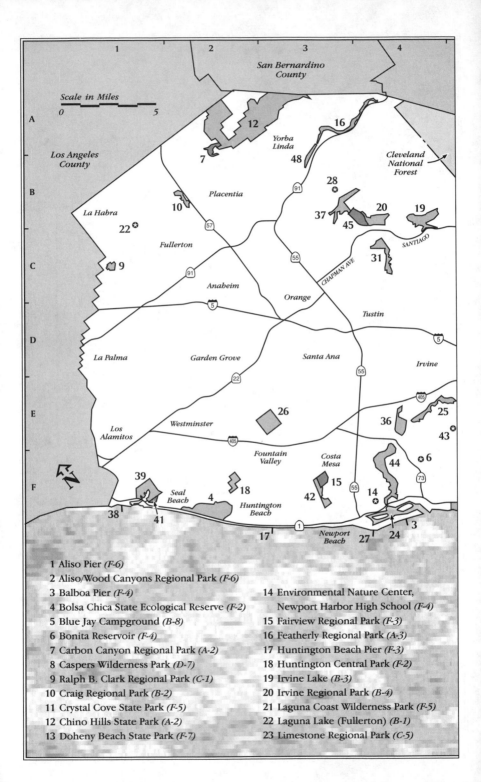

Scale in Miles
0   5

San Bernardino
County

Los Angeles
County

12

7

16

Yorba
Linda
48

Cleveland
National
Forest

28

91

37

20

19

10

Placentia

La Habra

22

45

SANTIAGO

Fullerton

9

91

31

Anaheim

55

CHAPMAN AVE.

5

Orange

Tustin

La Palma

Garden Grove

Santa Ana

Irvine

5

22

55

405

26

25

Westminster

36

43

Los
Alamitos

405

Fountain
Valley

Costa
Mesa

44

6

39

Seal
Beach

18

15

42

14

73

38

4

Huntington
Beach

1

17

Newport
Beach

27

24

3

41

1 Aliso Pier *(F-6)*

2 Aliso/Wood Canyons Regional Park *(F-6)*

3 Balboa Pier *(F-4)*

4 Bolsa Chica State Ecological Reserve *(F-2)*

5 Blue Jay Campground *(B-8)*

6 Bonita Reservoir *(F-4)*

7 Carbon Canyon Regional Park *(A-2)*

8 Caspers Wilderness Park *(D-7)*

9 Ralph B. Clark Regional Park *(C-1)*

10 Craig Regional Park *(B-2)*

11 Crystal Cove State Park *(F-5)*

12 Chino Hills State Park *(A-2)*

13 Doheny Beach State Park *(F-7)*

14 Environmental Nature Center,
Newport Harbor High School *(F-4)*

15 Fairview Regional Park *(F-3)*

16 Featherly Regional Park *(A-3)*

17 Huntington Beach Pier *(F-3)*

18 Huntington Central Park *(F-2)*

19 Irvine Lake *(B-3)*

20 Irvine Regional Park *(B-4)*

21 Laguna Coast Wilderness Park *(F-5)*

22 Laguna Lake (Fullerton) *(B-1)*

23 Limestone Regional Park *(C-5)*

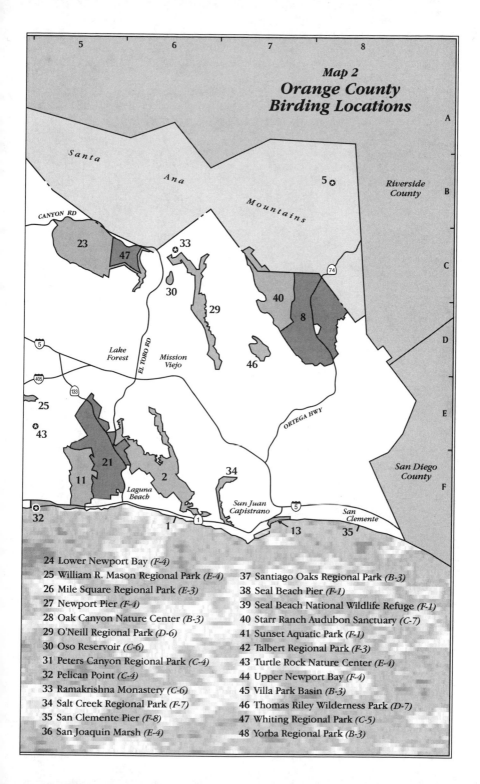

Map 2
Orange County Birding Locations

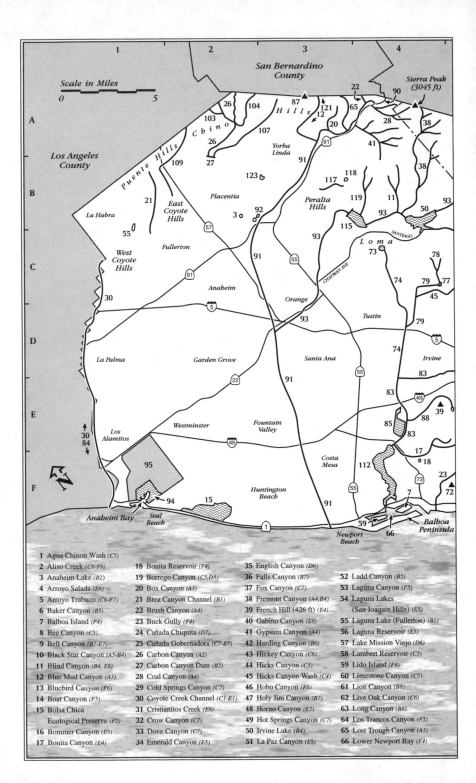

1 Agua Chinon Wash *(C5)*
2 Aliso Creek *(C6-F6)*
3 Anaheim Lake *(B2)*
4 Arroyo Salada *(E6)*
5 Arroyo Trabuco *(C6-F7)*
6 Baker Canyon *(B5)*
7 Balboa Island *(F4)*
8 Bee Canyon *(C5)*
9 Bell Canyon *(B7-E7)*
10 Black Star Canyon *(A5-B4)*
11 Blind Canyon *(B4, E8)*
12 Blue Mud Canyon *(A3)*
13 Bluebird Canyon *(F6)*
14 Boat Canyon *(F5)*
15 Bolsa Chica
   Ecological Preserve *(F2)*
16 Bommer Canyon *(E5)*
17 Bonita Canyon *(E4)*

18 Bonita Reservoir *(F4)*
19 Borrego Canyon *(C5,D5)*
20 Box Canyon *(A3)*
21 Brea Canyon Channel *(B1)*
22 Brush Canyon *(A4)*
23 Buck Gully *(F4)*
24 Cañada Chiquita *(D7)*
25 Cañada Gobernadora *(C7-E7)*
26 Carbon Canyon *(A2)*
27 Carbon Canyon Dam *(B2)*
28 Coal Canyon *(A4)*
29 Cold Springs Canyon *(C7)*
30 Coyote Creek Channel *(C1-E1)*
31 Cristianitos Creek *(E8)*
32 Crow Canyon *(C7)*
33 Dove Canyon *(C7)*
34 Emerald Canyon *(F5)*

35 English Canyon *(D6)*
36 Falls Canyon *(B7)*
37 Fox Canyon *(C7)*
38 Fremont Canyon *(A4,B4)*
39 French Hill (426 ft) *(E4)*
40 Gabino Canyon *(E8)*
41 Gypsum Canyon *(A4)*
42 Harding Canyon *(B6)*
43 Hickey Canyon *(C6)*
44 Hicks Canyon *(C5)*
45 Hicks Canyon Wash *(C4)*
46 Hobo Canyon *(F6)*
47 Holy Jim Canyon *(B7)*
48 Horno Canyon *(E7)*
49 Hot Springs Canyon *(C7)*
50 Irvine Lake *(B4)*
51 La Paz Canyon *(E8)*

52 Ladd Canyon *(B5)*
53 Laguna Canyon *(F5)*
54 Laguna Lakes
   (San Joaquin Hills) *(E5)*
55 Laguna Lake (Fullerton) *(B1)*
56 Laguna Reservoir *(E5)*
57 Lake Mission Viejo *(D6)*
58 Lambert Reservoir *(C5)*
59 Lido Island *(F4)*
60 Limestone Canyon *(C5)*
61 Lion Canyon *(B8)*
62 Live Oak Canyon *(C6)*
63 Long Canyon *(B8)*
64 Los Trancos Canyon *(F5)*
65 Lost Trough Canyon *(A3)*
66 Lower Newport Bay *(F4)*

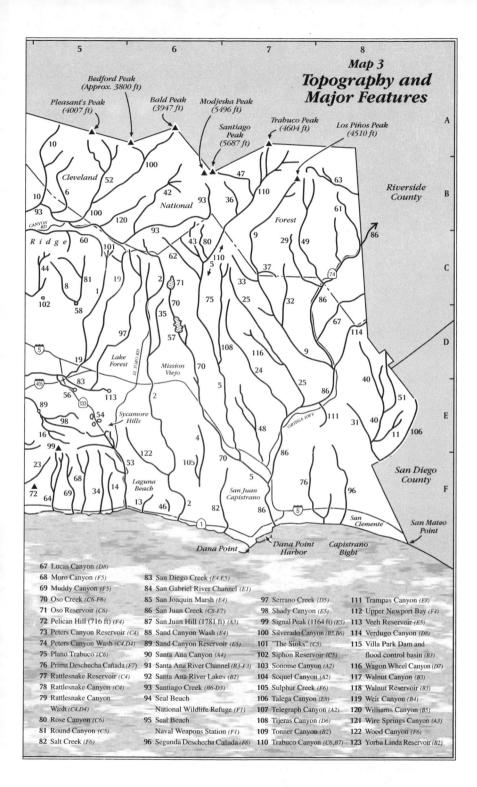

Map 3
Topography and Major Features

Bedford Peak (Approx. 3800 ft)

Pleasant's Peak (4007 ft)

Bald Peak (3947 ft)

Modjeska Peak (5496 ft)

Santiago Peak (5687 ft)

Trabuco Peak (4604 ft)

Los Piños Peak (4510 ft)

Riverside County

Cleveland

National

Forest

Ridge

CANYON RD

Lake Forest

Mission Viejo

Sycamore Hills

Laguna Beach

San Juan Capistrano

San Diego County

San Clemente

San Mateo Point

Dana Point

Dana Point Harbor

Capistrano Bight

EL TORO RD

ORTEGA HWY

67 Lucas Canyon *(D8)*
68 Moro Canyon *(F5)*
69 Muddy Canyon *(F5)*
70 Oso Creek *(C6-F6)*
71 Oso Reservoir *(C6)*
72 Pelican Hill (716 ft) *(F4)*
73 Peters Canyon Reservoir *(C4)*
74 Peters Canyon Wash *(C4,D4)*
75 Plano Trabuco *(C6)*
76 Prima Deschecha Cañada *(F7)*
77 Rattlesnake Reservoir *(C4)*
78 Rattlesnake Canyon *(C4)*
79 Rattlesnake Canyon Wash *(C4,D4)*
80 Rose Canyon *(C6)*
81 Round Canyon *(C5)*
82 Salt Creek *(F6)*

83 San Diego Creek *(E4,E5)*
84 San Gabriel River Channel *(E1)*
85 San Joaquin Marsh *(E4)*
86 San Juan Creek *(C8-F7)*
87 San Juan Hill (1781 ft) *(A3)*
88 Sand Canyon Wash *(E4)*
89 Sand Canyon Reservoir *(E5)*
90 Santa Ana Canyon *(A4)*
91 Santa Ana River Channel *(B3-F3)*
92 Santa Ana River Lakes *(B2)*
93 Santiago Creek *(B6-D3)*
94 Seal Beach National Wildlife Refuge *(F1)*
95 Seal Beach Naval Weapons Station *(F1)*
96 Segunda Deschecha Cañada *(F8)*

97 Serrano Creek *(D5)*
98 Shady Canyon *(E5)*
99 Signal Peak (1164 ft) *(E5)*
100 Silverado Canyon *(B5,B6)*
101 "The Sinks" *(C5)*
102 Siphon Reservoir *(C5)*
103 Sonome Canyon *(A2)*
104 Soquel Canyon *(A2)*
105 Sulphur Creek *(F6)*
106 Talega Canyon *(E8)*
107 Telegraph Canyon *(A2)*
108 Tijeras Canyon *(D6)*
109 Tonner Canyon *(B2)*
110 Trabuco Canyon *(C6,B7)*

111 Trampas Canyon *(E8)*
112 Upper Newport Bay *(F4)*
113 Veeh Reservoir *(E5)*
114 Verdugo Canyon *(D8)*
115 Villa Park Dam and flood control basin *(B3)*
116 Wagon Wheel Canyon *(D7)*
117 Walnut Canyon *(B3)*
118 Walnut Reservoir *(B3)*
119 Weir Canyon *(B4)*
120 Williams Canyon *(B5)*
121 Wire Springs Canyon *(A3)*
122 Wood Canyon *(F6)*
123 Yorba Linda Reservoir *(B2)*

Notes